Precast Concrete: Handling and Erection

AMERICAN CONCRETE INSTITUTE MONOGRAPH SERIES

Precast Concrete:
Handling and Erection

Joseph J. Waddell

PUBLISHED JOINTLY BY

THE IOWA STATE UNIVERSITY PRESS
AMES, IOWA
AMERICAN CONCRETE INSTITUTE
DETROIT, MICHIGAN

ACI Monograph No. 8

THIS MONOGRAPH is published in furtherance of ACI objectives in the fields of engineering education and technology. The Institute is not responsible for the statements or opinions expressed in its publications. Institute publications are not able to, nor intended to, supplant individual training, responsibility, or judgment of the user, or the supplier, of the information presented.

Library of Congress Cataloging in Publication Data
Waddell, Joseph J
   Precast concrete.
   (ACI monograph no. 8)
   Includes bibliographical references.
   1. Precast concrete.   2. Precast concrete construction.   I. Title.
   II. Series: American Concrete Institute monograph, no. 8.
TA683.7.W33   624′.1834   72–88703
ISBN 0–8138–1305–0

First edition, 1974

Printed in the United States of America

Also in this series:

Lessons from Failures of Concrete Structures, by Jacob Feld—ACI Monograph No. 1

Evaluation of Concrete Properties from Sonic Tests, by E. A. Whitehurst—ACI Monograph No. 2

Freezing and Thawing of Concrete—Mechanisms and Control, by William A. Cordon—ACI Monograph No. 3

Durability of Concrete Construction, by Hubert Woods—ACI Monograph No. 4

Design of Flexural Members for Static and Blast Loading, by J. R. Allgood and G. R. Swihart—ACI Monograph No. 5

Hardened Concrete: Physical and Mechanical Aspects, by Adam M. Neville—ACI Monograph No. 6

Better Concrete Pavement Serviceability, by Edwin A. Finney—ACI Monograph No. 7

ABOUT THE AUTHOR

JOSEPH J. WADDELL has long been recognized as a leading expert in the field of concrete materials and prestressed concrete. After obtaining the B.S. degree in engineering from the University of Arizona in 1929, he was employed in varied engineering capacities until 1934 when he joined the U.S. Bureau of Reclamation at Parker Dam, California, as a concrete and materials engineer.

From 1956 to 1961 he was chief materials engineer with Knoerle, Graef, Bender, and Associates, Inc., Chicago, Ill., consulting engineers for Illinois Toll Highway Program. In 1961 he joined Soils Testing Services, Inc., Chicago, Ill., as chief materials engineer. In 1963 he accepted the position of technical service engineer with the Riverside Cement Company of Los Angeles. After thirty-five years' experience in the concrete industry he retired in 1971.

Since he joined the ACI in 1938 he has written many articles for this group and for the American Society for Testing Materials. He is author of *Quality Control of Concrete,* author-editor of *The Concrete Construction Handbook,* and coauthor of *The Rotary Cement Kiln.*

Mr. Waddell served many years on the ACI committees 201, Durability of Concrete; 308, Curing Concrete; 311, Inspection of Concrete; 546, Repair of Concrete; and E-703, Manual of Instruction and Construction. He has served also as chairman of ACI committees 311 and E-703.

Preface

THE READER is cautioned that the drawings presented in this monograph are typical designs and should not be used as working drawings. Working drawings should be prepared by a qualified Architect/Engineer* in conformance with local conditions and code requirements. Some of these details are from actual working drawings but should be checked for compliance with any particular set of conditions on a specific project before being used. Special attention is directed to the sketches of assemblies and joinery. Many of these do not show the necessary reinforcement of connection details since these must be designed in accordance with local job and code requirements. Generally, construction practice requires that joints between precast concrete members, between precast and cast-in-place concrete, and between precast concrete and other structural elements incorporate some sort of a positive connection that will transmit the imposed loads safely.

The author wishes to thank the following associations and firms who generously furnished illustrations and data in their equipment and jobs:

Aerovac Corporation, Burke Concrete Accessories, Inc., Drott Manufacturing Co., Midwest Prestressed Concrete Co., Mo-Sai In-

---

* In this book the term "Architect/Engineer" refers to the architect, the engineer, or both, in accordance with their professional agreement.

stitute, Northwest Engineering Co., Olympian Stone Co., Pitman Division of A. B. Chance Co., Portland Cement Association, Preco Industries, Ltd., Prestressed Concrete Manufacturers Association of California, Progressive Transportation Co., Rockwin Schokbeton, and Superior Concrete Accessories, Inc.

Contents

Precast Concrete:
Handling and Erection

1

GENERAL
CONSIDERATIONS

PRECAST CONCRETE HAS BEEN in use since the latter part of the 19th century. Many of the early structures were marine installations as well as bridges and buildings.[1] Development has been continuous, and now that concrete has emerged as a highly ornamental and useful construction material, today we see convincing evidence of the dramatic effects possible with its use. This imposes an obligation on the concrete construction industry, an obligation that was aptly voiced by Minoru Yamasaki:[2]

> Precast concrete is the most exciting of structural materials; it is the future of structure. This is true not only in dramatic spans but in ordinary, everyday buildings.
> My major indictment of the concrete industry is that it persists in thinking of its product as a crude material. No building should be built crudely; all good architecture throughout history has been fine and elegant. This can and should be attained with concrete, and with precast concrete both elegance and economy are possible. We as a society should be mature enough to provide ourelves with beautiful surroundings. Beauty is not a matter of cost; its attainment rests on discrimination in selection.

During the last two decades there has been a succession of advances in the state-of-the-art of precasting that has been responsible for an impressive gain in the use of precast concrete. Coupled with this improvement in equipment and methods (which results in a saving in cost) is a freedom for aesthetic expression in shapes, sizes, textures, and colors that gives the architect a practical construction material offering unlimited possibilities for imparting beauty and ornamentation to concrete structures.

Precast concrete today is the result of a partnership of architect, structural engineer, precaster, materials supplier, and contractor, each of whom does his part in creating a structure that is an exciting rendition of an artistic idea into enduring form and substance.

SYSTEMS BUILDING CONCEPT

In the systems building concept, all features of the building are analyzed so that the design, manufacture, on-site operations, and overall administration can be coordinated into a unified system. The idea of systems building is not limited to concrete, although concrete plays an important role in its application, involving extensive use of precast concrete—either plant precast or on-site precast.

Although precasting and prefabrication have been in use for many years, the concept of systems building made great strides in Europe just after World War II when it became necessary to provide mass housing for thousands of persons made homeless by the war's destruction. The method has since spread throughout the world. Individual housing units now constitute a small segment of the systems method; schools and apartments have especially benefitted.

The capacity of the building industry in North America has to be increased to take care of the growing demand for housing, schools, and other facilities. Systems building (that is, prefabrication) is becoming more necessary every day. The field is constantly changing, with new systems being developed and old ones discarded.

No attempt is made in this monograph to cover in detail the methods of handling and erecting the components of any particular type of building system. The methods and equipment described herein, however, being considered from the standpoint of precast concrete construction, are adaptable to use in any of the systems. The several basic types of systems are:

1. Post and beam, consisting of prefabricated columns and beams with panels

2. Slab or panel, usually consisting of precast panels (either horizontal, vertical, or both) with other components either precast with the panels or cast in place

3. Box, consisting of different sizes of precast three-dimensional structural members, some of them including preinstalled service features

4. Units or components of any type, with fully compatible subsystems, manufactured to comply with a specification that defines performance instead of defining the units.

A special language has developed along with development of the systems.[3,4,5] The definitions given below will be of value.

1. *Systems (or industrialized) building*—The integration of planning, design, programming, manufacturing, site operations, scheduling, financing, and management into a disciplined method of mechanized production of buildings.

2. *Rationalized traditional system*—One that depends primarily on conventional skilled trades but which incorporates mechanization and prefabricated components.

3. *Building system*—The method by which a variety of structural and mechanical units is assembled, erected, and installed to produce structures that will function for a specified use or combination of uses.

4. *Open system*—One in which the components are interchangeable with those of other systems.

5. *Closed system*—One in which the components are peculiar to that system and cannot be combined with those of another system.

6. *Prefabrication*—Factory assembly of structural, mechanical, or electrical components or complete and fully equipped structures (such as mobile homes).

7. *Component*—A factory or site-produced unit designed to perform specified tasks.

8. *Subsystem*—A group of factory or site-assembled components erected or installed in combination with each other to perform a specified task.

9. *Dimensional (or modular) coordination*—Reduction of the size of all building components and buildings to multiples of one basic unit.

PRECAST UNITS

Units can be classified as to types (such as tees or cored slabs), or they can be classified as to function (such as curtainwalls or structural beams). Some are prestressed, either by pretensioning or post-tensioning, and others contain conventional reinforcement. They may be further classified as structural load-bearing units or non-load-bearing units. For instance, windowwalls can be produced to fit into either the load-bearing or non-load-bearing category depending on the design. However, one unit will be designed to carry part of the building load, while on another building a similar unit would be supported on the building frame and would not contribute to the strength of the structure. The difference would not be apparent to the casual observer of the finished building (Fig. 1.1).

A load-bearing member is a unit that carries or supports part of the weight and live load of the structure other than its own weight. A non-load-bearing member is one that is attached to and supported by the building frame; it may or may not support its own weight.

Types of Units

The following tabulation provides a general framework for classifying precast concrete units. However, there is a certain overlapping, and one particular manufactured unit may well be classified in more than one category.

Curtainwalls—A curtainwall unit, shown in Fig. 1.2, is a complete wall unit that can be attached to the structural frame to enclose the building. Both sides are finished, and insulation can be cast sandwich style in the unit or attached to the interior. Accommodations for mechanical service facilities can be cast into the units.

Windowwalls—Extending over one, two, or three stories and as wide as 20 ft, windowwalls consist of spandrels, mullions, and related nonstructural elements that constitute a complete wall enclosure, ready for glazing (see Figs. 1.3, 6.8, and 6.9). Aluminum or other window frames can be set into rabbets formed in the concrete; or the glass, with proper gaskets, can be set directly into slots in the concrete. It is sometimes possible to glaze the units at the casting plant. Some windowwalls are structurally load-bearing, some are not.

Forms for cast-in-place concrete—Off-site casting of building units can sometimes be expedited by on-site casting of thin sections with architectural rendering on the outside, the units being U or L shaped, flat, or hollow. Anchor-

Fig. 1.1—Typical of the beauty of white precast concrete is this municipal office building.

Fig. 1.2—Curtainwall units being installed.

ages, cast in the precast concrete, serve as anchors for ties to hold the form together or attach it to the structural frame. Dowels and tie-bars are usually specified. Concrete is placed within the precast form after attachment of the form to the building frame, as shown in Fig. 1.4.

Screenwall, grilles, or solar screens—These are nonstructural units, highly ornamented, used for sun screens or as space dividers. They are pierced with numerous openings to provide for air movement. Figure 1.5 is a good example. They may be used for purely ornamental enclosures or for hiding certain problem areas. Concrete masonry is also used for this purpose.

Framing members—These are load-bearing elements that form part of the structural frame of the building, and many are prestressed. They might be simple columns, beams, joists, arches, ribs, or combinations of some of these. For example, a spandrel beam can be cast integrally with a column. Precast and prestressed beams, girders, and slabs for bridges and similar structures come within this category (see Fig. 5.3).

Facing—Precast concrete can add new life and beauty by modernizing obsolete exteriors of buildings that are still functional on the interior. Many old buildings are structurally sound and can be restored to new years of useful life by such treatment (Fig. 1.6). Anchors, cast integrally in the facing units, make it a simple matter to attach the facing to the concrete, steel, or masonry structure.

Fig. 1.3—A windowwall member being hoisted into place.

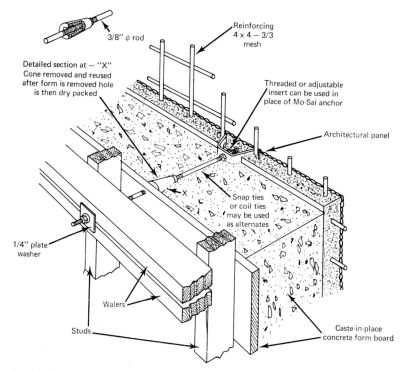

3/8″ φ rod

Reinforcing
4 x 4 – 3/3
mesh

Detailed section at – "X"
Cone removed and reused
after form is removed hole
is then dry packed

Threaded or adjustable
insert can be used in
place of Mo-Sai anchor

Architectural panel

X

Snap ties
or coil ties
may be used
as alternates

1/4″ plate
washer

Walers

Studs

Caste-in-place
concrete form board

Fig. 1.4—Precast concrete can be used as a form for cast-in-place concrete.

Windowwalls and curtainwalls lend themselves especially well to this application.

Tees—Tees are prestressed single or multiple units for floors and roofs (Fig. 1.7a and b). Single tees are generally large members for spans of 30 ft or more. Spans of some single tees have exceeded 100 ft. Double tees are used for medium spans. Modifications such as channels, F-sections, multiple tees, and "gull wing" or Y-shape are available from some producers.

Girders, beams, and joists—These are structural load-bearing members and may be solid rectangular, hollow box, I-beam, T-beam, keystone, ledger beam, or some modification. Spans of well over 100 ft are typical; small joists might span 12 ft or less.

Planks and slabs—Used for roofs and floors, these units are often prestressed. They might be extruded or wet-cast in long lengths and sawed into appropriate parts for the job. Slabs are either solid or cored, in widths ranging from 16 to 48 in., usually 6 or 8 in. thick, rarely 4 or 12 in. thick. Such units span about 50 ft. Planks are solid, 3 in. or less in thickness, and used for short spans. They are frequently used as bottom forms for cast-in-place decks or floors.

Ornamental units—Fasciae and bas-relief panels for a high degree of artistic expression are possible and can be anchored to the building frame. These can serve as forms for cast-in-place concrete.

Fig. 1.5—This screenwall is attached about 18 in. away from the wall of the building, supported on pilasters and attached at the top.

Fig. 1.6—Mo-Sai exposed aggregate facing panels being erected to modernize an old building.

Tank segments—Precast tanks or reservoirs consist of an assemblage of identical barrel-shell segments set vertically with the convex side of the shell facing inward.

Miscellaneous architectural units—Many small specialized pieces can be cast, including small ornaments, sills, mullions, lintels, and columns.

Other items precasting plants produce—These include piles of various cross sections, sheet piling, powerline poles, lighting standards, railroad cross ties, cribbing, road dividers, and stadium seats.

ON-SITE PRECASTING

Although we are not directly concerned with manufacture of precast concrete, a brief mention of on-site precasting is in order.

On-site precasting had a modest beginning, when some contractors found they could fabricate post-tensioned girders on the site. These were usually large and heavy girders for bridges. The idea caught on when the economies and convenience of the concept became obvious; it is now a well-established construction practice of some progressive building contractors. It is particularly adaptable to a building in which the variety of units can be kept at a minimum but the quantity of each type of unit can be maximized.

The on-site precaster has at least one advantage: he does not have to move his elements from the casting yard over the highway to the building site. Items cast off-site require special hauling

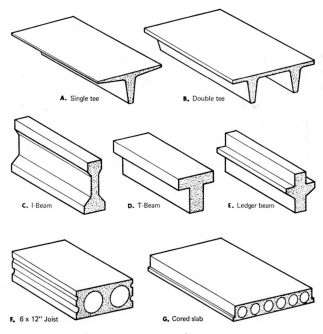

A. Single tee   B. Double tee

C. I-Beam   D. T-Beam   E. Ledger beam

F. 6 x 12" Joist   G. Cored slab

Fig. 1.7—Several types of precast concrete units.

vehicles because of their size, weight, or unwieldy dimensions. Whether on-site precasting for a particular project will be economically done requires careful analysis of all factors involved. First, one must determine the space required for casting and storage. Second, one must consider the cost of casting beds, forms, prestressing facilities, concrete placing and curing facilities, and installation of special cranes. A third consideration is assembly of a specialized crew. One other basic requirement is the repetitive manufacturing of identical units to make the most efficient use of casting and handling equipment.

Advantages of on-site precasting include the convenience of adjusting production schedules on short notice to conform to changes in erection operations. More efficient use of personnel is possible, because workmen can be transferred from the precasting work to the construction site as the work load and other conditions vary from time to time. Construction time can be decreased, and the possibility of delays in construction resulting from delays in delivery of certain units is reduced. When properly applied to a building designed for this type of construction, the method is efficient and economical. Beams, columns, windowwalls, and other shapes can be successfully executed.

One system makes use of floor slabs precast on the site in stacks, one on top of the other. This system is particularly adaptable for hotels and apartments, in which the slabs can be room size so they reach from outside wall to corridor partition and between adjacent partitions.

 Construction Sequence

The slabs are cast at a convenient location adjacent to the building. Casting of slabs can proceed while concrete for foundation and slab-on-grade is being placed. First-floor walls are constructed to the elevation of the ceiling and topped off in some manner to accept the precast slabs (Fig. 1.8). After concrete in the precast slabs and in the walls develops adequate strength, the slab is lifted by crane and set in place on the cast-in-place walls. Tie-bars extending from the edges of the slab are bent up so that, when reinforcing steel is placed for the next story wall, the bent tie-bars will be hooked over the lowest horizontal bar. The wall is then formed in the usual manner: a grout layer is placed in the bottom

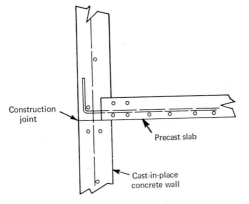

Fig. 1.8—Typical joinery of precast floor slab and cast-in-place wall.

Construction joint

Precast slab

Cast-in-place concrete wall

of the form to cover the previously placed wall concrete and the end of the precast slab; then wall concrete is cast. Each subsequent story and the roof are constructed in the same manner.

If care is used in casting, the bottom side of the slab can serve as the ceiling of the story below and can be sprayed with an acoustical treatment. Floor covering can be attached directly to the top side.

RESPONSIBILITIES

In the manufacture and erection of precast concrete, responsibilities of all members of the team must be clearly defined to minimize the overlapping of responsibilities, or worse—the failure to assign a certain responsibility. Once the responsibilities have been defined, the job will proceed harmoniously.

The Architect/Engineer has the overall responsibility for completion of the structure or building in accordance with the plans and specifications prepared by him to satisfy the needs of the owner.

Today the general idea is to divide the responsibility among the specialists who perform the several functions. In this concept the general contractor has the responsibility to select the precaster, erector, and caulker. The precaster then becomes responsible for design of the units to resist stresses resulting from manufacturing, handling, and erection. This does not usurp or supersede the responsibility of the Architect/Engineer for the basic integrity of the structure. The precaster should furnish all items of hardware to be embedded in the precast units and is required to furnish units of the proper size, configuration, color, and texture in clean and undamaged condition. The carrier shares the responsibility for proper and safe delivery of the units to the job site. The following outline shows how the sharing of responsibility can be achieved. There are no fixed rules on this, and any decision as to responsibility should be agreed to at the very start of the job. This list is by no means complete and is given merely to indicate the rather complex lines of communication that must be kept open during the construction period to keep the job moving on schedule.

One of the first obligations to be fulfilled, once the go-ahead is received, is the preparation of shop drawings. The supplier of precast concrete is required to furnish shop drawings showing complete information for casting and installing the units, including location and types of all fittings, inserts, and anchors. Details and locations for supports for storing and hauling should be shown. If extra reinforcement is required in any of the units to withstand handling stresses, details should be shown on the shop drawings. The general contractor should check these drawings to be sure they contain all the essential information and are dimensionally accurate, including allowance for tolerances. After the shop drawings have been checked by the general contractor, they are sent to the Architect/Engineer for approval. The general contractor usually prepares erection and placing plans, including handling, temporary bracing, location in the structure, connections, and caulking details; he should have the drawings checked by all trades involved with the job to assure adequacy and accuracy of openings, embedded items, and similar details.

The precaster must identify each member by marking it clearly and legibly, in accordance with the erection plan. There are many brands of black nonfading ink or paint that can be applied with a brush or special felt-tip marker. Markings should be clearly visible while the units are stored in the yard and while on the delivery vehicle but should be on surfaces not to be exposed to view in the finished structure. It may be several weeks or months before a unit is installed, and a faded or obliterated identification mark can be a source of frustration and delay. Other items of responsibility are listed below.

How these units are cast is not within the scope of this monograph. Our interest begins after these units have been removed from the forms and stored in the casting yard.

Item	Responsibility
Design of the structure	Architect/Engineer
Manufacture of the precast units	Precast manufacturer. Assigned by general contractor and approved by Architect/Engineer.
Design of connections	Architect/Engineer. Precaster reviews for tolerances and feasibility.
Design of units to resist manufacturing, handling, and erection stresses	Precaster. Reviewed by Architect/Engineer.
Furnishing connections, anchors, and other hardware	Precaster furnishes all items to be embedded in the precast concrete and all items of attachment hardware at the job site. General contractor furnishes all items to be embedded in the structural frame.
Condition of the units	Precaster delivers clean and undamaged units to the job site. General contractor protects the units from soiling and damage after delivery. Erector is responsible during erection.
Erection	General contractor. Usually assigned to a subcontractor by general contractor or precaster.
Sequence of erection	In some cases the Architect/Engineer will specify sequence of erection because of effect of partially completed construction on the structure. For example, panels supported on floors might cause excessive deflection of the floor if precautions are not taken to minimize the deflection by controlling erection sequence.

Item	Responsibility
Caulking	General contractor. Usually assigned to a subcontractor by general contractor or precaster.
Aesthetic appearance	Architect/Engineer is responsible for the design. Precaster is responsible for the execution.

2
TILT-UP

Tɪʟᴛ-ᴜᴘ ɪs ᴀ ᴛʏᴘᴇ of precast construction in which wall panels are cast in a horizontal position at the site and tilted to a vertical position to become part of the building (Fig. 2.1). A special application is one in which the panels may be tilted and then moved horizontally with a crane. Generally, the concrete floor of the building serves as the casting platform. Columns are cast in place after the panels have been erected. Panels may be of solid concrete or of sandwich construction in which relatively thin, high-strength conventional concrete surfacing layers are separated by a core of low-density insulating material. Although tilt-up is occasionally used for small residential construction, its principal application is for commercial and industrial buildings.

HARDWARE

The same basic inserts and anchors that are discussed at length under "Lifting Hardware" in Chapter 3 are used in tilt-up construction. Some manufacturers make items especially designed for this application, as shown in Fig. 2.2. Note that each item consists of two parts: (1) the anchor that remains embedded in the

Fig. 2.1—A panel being tilted, with the crane outside the building area.

concrete and (2) the attachment element that is bolted into the anchor.

The single insert (Fig. 2.2a) is the most widely used insert and is adapted for use with the swivel lifting plate (Fig. 2.2c). For unusually large or heavy panels, angle lifting plates (Fig. 2.2b) are employed with the double insert (Fig. 2.2e). Figure 2.2d shows a double-edge insert.

Inserts are usually sized to set back 3/8 in. from the top face of the panel, but exposed aggregate panels or other panels with irregular surfaces require special treatment. When attaching a lifting plate to an exposed aggregate panel, immediately after washing is

a

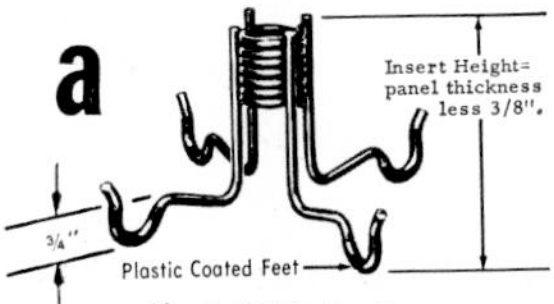
Insert Height= panel thickness less 3/8".
3/4"
Plastic Coated Feet

Single Pick-Up Insert

b

ANGLE LIFTING PLATE

Available in sizes as shown, the angle lifting plate is to be used with the double pick-up insert.

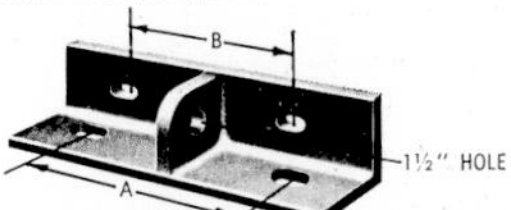
B
1½" HOLE
A

	For use with 1" Type D Inserts only (Available from West Coast warehouses only)	For use with 1½" Type D Inserts only (Available from West Coast warehouses only)	For use with either 1" Type D Inserts or 1½" Type D Inserts (Available from Franklin Park warehouse only)*
Dimension A	12"	15"	15"
Dimension B	—	—	12"
Angle Size	3½"x5"x⅜"x18"	4"x6"x¾"x21"	6"x6"x¾"x21"
Slotted hole size	1¹⁄₁₆"x2"	1⁹⁄₁₆"x2½"	1¹⁄₁₆"x2" and 1⁹⁄₁₆"x2½"
Minimum Coil Bolt length for lifting	1"x4"	1½"x4"	1"x4" or 1½"x4"
Weight (each)	28 lbs.	47 lbs.	53 lbs.

Use of cut washer is recommended *Illustrated above
Longer length coil bolts will be required for exposed aggregate panels. See page 8 for details.

D=Minimum length of Coil Bolt for lifting. (Use of cut washer is recommended.)

Longer length coil bolts will be required for exposed aggregate panels. See page 8 for details.

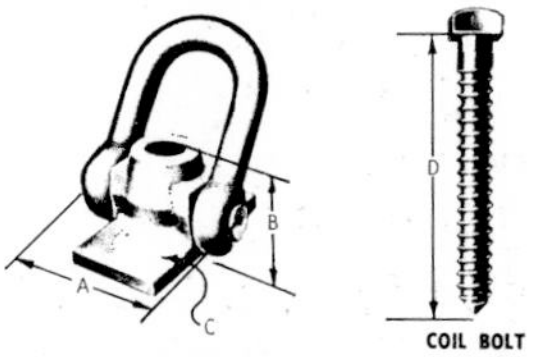
B
A
C
D
COIL BOLT

c

SWIVEL LIFTING PLATE

For use with Type S Single Pick-Up Insert, the Swivel Lifting Plate is a steel forging to which a heavy steel bearing plate has been welded. The shackle is forged of 1" diameter stock and swings on a line through the center of the bolt.

SIZE and Wt.		A	B	C	D	Ultimate Capacity (Lifting Plate Only)
¾"	4 lbs.	5"	1⅜"	½x2½x5	4"	45,000 lbs.
1"	4 lbs.	5"	1⅜"	½x2½x5	5"	45,000 lbs.
1½"	10 lbs.	6"	2½"	½x3x6	6"	60,000 lbs.

d

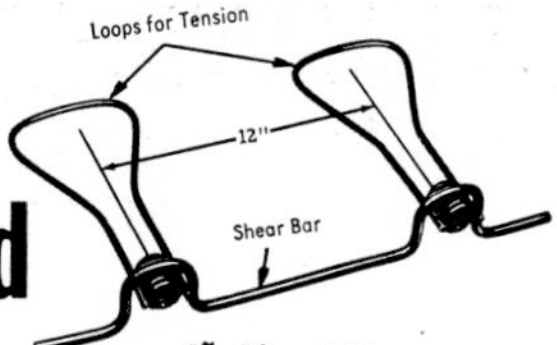
Loops for Tension
12"
Shear Bar

1" Edge Pick-Up Insert

e

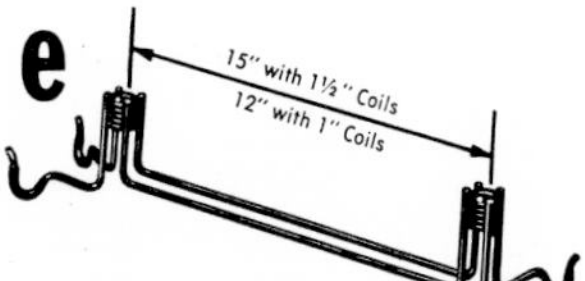
15" with 1½" Coils
12" with 1" Coils

Double Pick-Up Insert

f

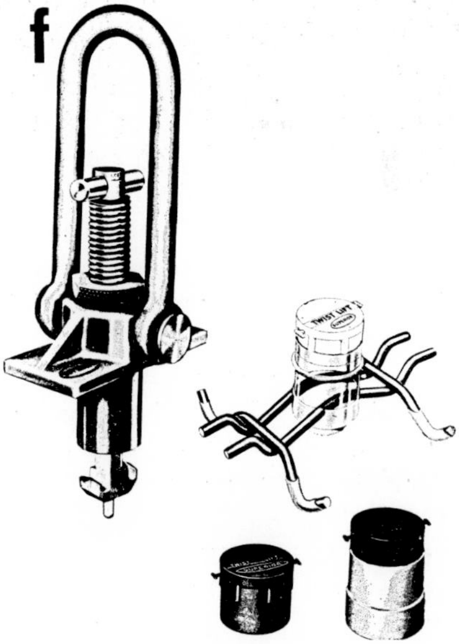

Fig. 2.2—Several basic items of hardware for tilt-up work.

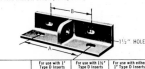

completed, place a piece of 6 mil polyethylene sheeting over the insert area; then install a coil bolt to prevent grout leakage into the coils of the insert. Prepare a mortar mixture and cast a pad, 1 or 2 in. thick, on top of the film. The pad should extend about 2 in. beyond the lift plate in all directions and be troweled to a smooth surface. When the panel is ready for tilting, remove the template bolts and attach the lifting plate with the proper length of coil bolts. Longer than normal coil bolts will be required because of the thickness of the mortar pad. The pad will fall off the panel when the lifting plate is removed. Strength of the pad must be equal to that of the panel concrete at the time of lift.

Another lifting unit insert combination is depicted in Fig. 2.2f. A plastic sleeve and cap, attached to the insert, is removed just before making the lift. A bushing on the lifting hardware fits into the hole left by the plastic sleeve, and a steel locking hook engages the insert. The hardware is then adjusted by hand, and the crane hook is attached to the bail to make the lift. Hardware on all these units is removed for additional use, and the insert hole is filled with dry tamped mortar.

RIGGING

Size and weight of the panel are the primary considerations influencing the selection and location of lifting hardware. Other factors are number, size, and location of openings in the panel; design strength of the concrete; whether the lift will be made from inside or outside the building; type of crane or other lifting equipment; cost of alternate arrangements; and time and labor required to attach and remove the hardware.

There are several methods used for designating the number of pickup points in a panel and their arrangement which, because of differences in description, might lead to some confusion. For example, the two-wide, two-high arrangement shown in Fig. 2.3 can also be designated "double-row four-point," "four-point double-line," or simply "2 x 2 pickup." The two-wide, four-high layout in Fig. 2.4 is variously known at four-row, eight-point, or 2 x 2 x 2 x 2 pickup. If we use the "wide and high" designation, identification is simplified and standardized. This method will be used in this book. Large and heavy panels may have a four-wide, four-high pickup consisting of sixteen pickup points. The simplest

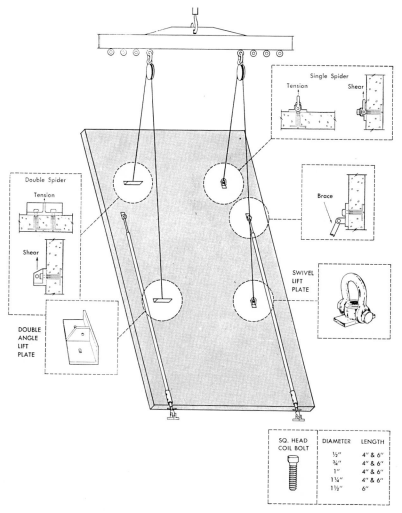

Fig. 2.3—The most common rigging, sometimes called a 2 x 2 pickup, is a simple system consisting of two points horizontally and two rows vertically.

is a two-wide, one-high arrangement. Other arrangements are also shown in Fig. 2.4.

Job operations can be simplified if all the panels in the building are considered in the design of a rigging layout, in order to develop a pickup suitable to the majority of panels. For example, there may be a few panels that require a two-high pickup but most

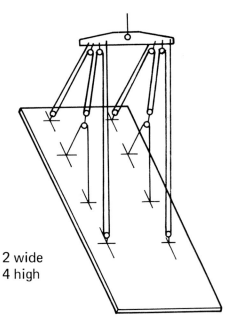

Fig. 2.4—Four pickup arrangements for flat panels of varying sizes and weights.

2 wide
4 high

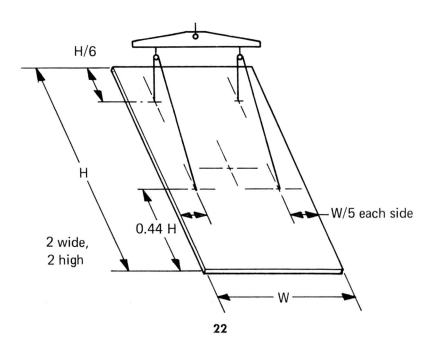

H/6

H

2 wide,
2 high

0.44 H

W/5 each side

W

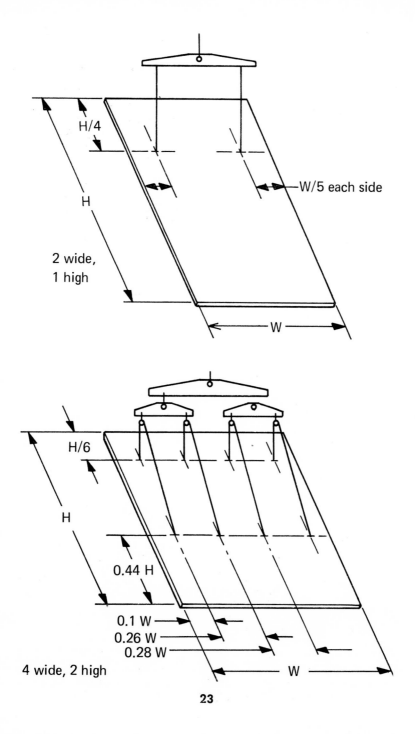

H/4

H

W/5 each side

2 wide,
1 high

W

H/6

H

0.44 H

0.1 W
0.26 W
0.28 W

4 wide, 2 high

W

of them require a three-high pickup. It may be more economical
to rig all the panels the same way with the three-high system to
save time on the job in changing from one system to the other.

Figure 2.3 shows a plain tilt-up panel with simple two-wide,
two-high rigging, details of several items of lifting hardware, and
two temporary braces. This is the rigging most frequently used.
Basic rigging is called a two-wide single-row lift and can be accomplished by attaching two inserts about a quarter to a third of
the way down from the top of the panel. In this way the panel
will hang nearly vertical when it is lifted. This pickup can be used
for panels up to about 18 ft wide and 18 ft high. Another two-point
pickup is the top pickup, or edge lift, shown in Fig. 2.5. In the
edge lift, the edge of the panel must be protected from spalling
and breakage. This can be done in several ways. Some manufacturers of hardware make an anchorage that is especially designed
to be inserted in edge concrete. Some precasters place a reinforcing
bar in the panel about 2 in. from and parallel to the end; some

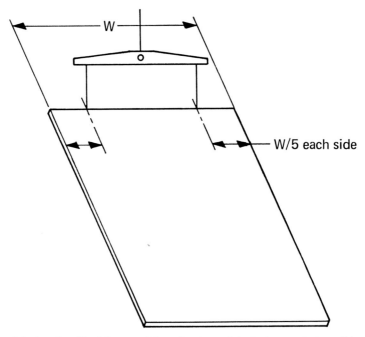

Fig. 2.5—An edge lift pickup consisting of a two-point, single-row rigging. This system can be used on heavy panels provided sufficient reinforcement is supplied to resist the bending stresses when the panel is lifted.

precasters bolt a channel or angle to the top edge of the panel to which the lifting lines are attached.

These are but a few of the possible arrangements. A structural analysis is necessary for determining the exact location of pickup points, with the horizontal spacing determined by panel width, and the panel height fixing the number of rows of inserts. Ordinarily, three-wide rigging is not recommended because of the difficulty in making three cables exactly the same length, although one of the riggings shown in Fig. 2.6 can be used. For panels that are too wide for a two-wide pickup, a four-wide pickup, using three spreaders, can be used.

Loadings on inserts must be balanced, accomplished by using spreaders and passing flexible wire ropes over sheaves to equalize the loadings. In every case the center of rigging must remain over a vertical line on the panel through its center of gravity. If this is not done, the panel will not hang level, which will cause unequal loading on the inserts and placing problems.

In a symmetrical panel (for example, a rectangular or square panel without openings) the center of gravity lies on the vertical

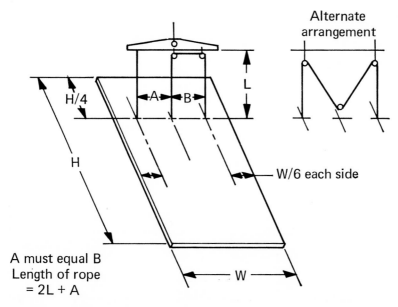

Fig. 2.6—Three-wide rigging is ordinarily not recommended, although one of these arrangements can be used (see Fig. 2.11).

center line. This is true also for a panel with an opening or openings symmetrical about the center line. For an asymmetrical panel it is necessary to compute the location of the center of gravity. This is accomplished in the usual manner by considering the entire panel without openings as a positive area and the openings as negative areas, then taking the summation of the X and Y coordinates to the centers of the openings and the panel to find the center of gravity.

As shown in Fig. 2.7, a table can be set up for any number of openings in the panel and the summation of areas determined from which the coordinates of the center of gravity can be computed. In

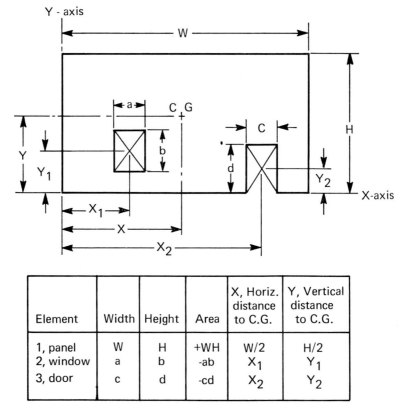

Element	Width	Height	Area	X, Horiz. distance to C.G.	Y, Vertical distance to C.G.
1, panel	W	H	+WH	W/2	H/2
2, window	a	b	-ab	X_1	Y_1
3, door	c	d	-cd	X_2	Y_2

Fig. 2.7—Computations for determining the center of gravity of an asymmetrical panel can be simplified by setting up a table, then using the equations.

a rectangular panel with one window opening, the equations for the coordinates of the center of gravity are

$$X = \frac{\dfrac{W^2H}{2} - abX_1}{WH - ab}$$

and

$$Y = \frac{\dfrac{WH^2}{2} - abY_1}{WH - ab}$$

If there are openings in the panel for a window and a door, the equations become

$$X = \frac{\dfrac{W^2H}{2} - abX_1 - cdX_2}{WH - (ab + cd)}$$

and

$$Y = \frac{\dfrac{WH^2}{2} - abY_1 - cdY_2}{WH - (ab + cd)}$$

These equations can be further developed to fit any combination of openings in a flat panel.

From the weight of the panel and the manufacturer's description of the inserts, we can determine the type, number, and location of the inserts. Inserts should be placed at points that will minimize bending moments.

Tilting causes stresses in the concrete in excess of what is required for structural design, and it is necessary to make sure that the panel has reached adequate strength with a factor of safety before being tilted. Field-cured cylinders or nondestructive tests of the panel concrete will provide this information. Pickup points must be located carefully and lifting equipment must be designed to avoid high localized stresses in the panel that can cause cracking, spalling, or splitting of the concrete. Vacuum lifting attachments are used sometimes (see Chapter 3).

More lifting force may be required to break the panel loose from the casting floor than is necessary to lift the panel after movement is started. Before lifting, the panel can be moved slightly with jacks operating in a horizontal direction, sliding the panel a fraction of an inch to break the bond.

TILTING

The operation of lifting the panel is usually the only time the panel is handled. The initial lift imposes a tensile load on the lifting anchors, possibly coupled with a low value of shear. As the panel is raised, tension decreases and shear increases, until practically the entire stress on the anchors is in shear when the panel is in a vertical position. Thus, the anchors and attachments should be designed to provide for shear rather than for tension; this will require larger bolts.

Various types of cranes, gin poles, and other arrangements have been used for tilting, but a mobile truck crane will usually be found to be best. An experienced crew is a necessity. This is especially so for the crane operator, whose skill can make the difference between a smooth-running job and delays. Although not required on all lifts, outriggers should be provided with the crane to be available when needed.

The method of tilting depends on whether the lift is made from the outside of the building or from the inside. Both methods are used (Figs. 2.1 and 2.8). Whether the panels have been cast face up or face down determines the choice of crane location. Probably most jobs are set up so the crane can operate from the inside, which necessitates preplanning so the floor can be designed to support the loads imposed by the crane. It is certainly advantageous to have the smooth operating area that the floor provides.

Preparations for tilting should be completed before the crane is scheduled to arrive on the job, to prevent expensive standby time for the crane. The setting pads, footing wall, or other base on which the panels are to rest should be cured and dry. Inserts on the panels should be located and cleaned, with anchors attached. Braces should be ready and available.

Fig. 2.8—General view of a tilt-up job, showing panels temporarily braced while the crane is moving another panel to be set up.

Lifting must be steady and even, avoiding sudden jerks that might overstress the concrete. Keeping the crane lines nearly vertical minimizes the danger of sliding the panel on the floor. Sliding must be avoided, not only because of the safety hazard but also because of possible damage to the panel. This is especially important if a special textured finish has been applied to the panel. Cables must be flexible and the blocks in smooth running condition so the rigging can adjust to maintain equal loading as the panel is tilted. The greatest force is that required to break the panel away from the casting floor; the remainder of the lift is relatively easy. During tilting, part of the weight of the panel is supported by the ground or floor.

It is common practice to set the panel on mortar erection or leveling pads that are finished to exact elevation, thus eliminating the need for precise leveling of the foundation wall. The foundation of course must be wide enough to accommodate the panels, usually at least 2 in. wider than the panel thickness. Pads should be located so the center of loading is at least 18 in. from the corner of the panel to eliminate the danger of diagonal cracks in the panel.

After the panels have been erected, the voids between the panel and foundation can be dry-packed or filled with plastic mortar to provide a weathertight seal.

Some contractors prefer to set the panel on a bed of fresh mortar on the foundation. After the panel has been erected, the mortar joint can be finished to make it watertight. Another variation, which is somewhat expensive and does not lend itself to precise adjustment of the panel, is to set the panel on a strip of premolded joint filler with a width about one-half to two-thirds the thickness of the panel. The open part of the joint is dry-packed after final setting of the panel.

Once the panel has been set on the pad footings, slight adjustments can be made to bring it into final alignment. Avoid the use of pinch bars or similar tools against the concrete, because they may spall the concrete. Bracing should be attached to the panel and the floor as soon as possible so the crane can be unhooked to pick up the next panel.

STRONGBACKS AND BRACES

Strongbacks can be attached to the panel for reinforcement to reduce stresses in the concrete during tilting. They are not necessary on most panels, and their use is usually confined to panels with openings where the remaining concrete is not of sufficient section to accommodate the tilting stresses. They are particularly desirable in the situation shown in Fig. 2.9 in which the length of the bearing surface on the leg is less than half the width of the panel. Two strongbacks normally are used, extending from top to bottom of the panel, sometimes with a cross member near the top.

Strongbacks can be made of 2-in. timber or steel shapes. A common arrangement consists of two 2-in. timbers or steel channels back-to-back with a space between through which the anchors are fastened (Fig. 2.10). Disadvantages are the time required to attach and remove them and disfiguration of the concrete surface with anchor holes that have to be patched.

The panel, after being tilted to a vertical position in its final location, must be well braced until the cast-in-place concrete in the columns has developed its design strength. All panels must be well braced at the end of each day's work. Do not leave overnight a panel only partly braced. End hardware for braces is made by

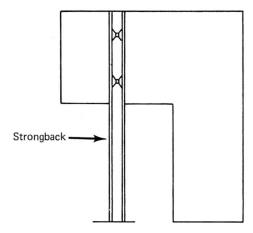

Fig. 2.9—A strongback is used to support the dangling arm of an irregular panel. A post shore should be provided behind the strongback to support the concrete after erection of the panel.

Strongback ⟶

several manufacturers for either metal or timber braces; some items can be fabricated in the shop on the job. Parts for each brace include an anchor embedded in the concrete of the panel, a wall bracket that fits on the end of the brace and is attached to the anchor, a floor bracket that includes a screw jack or turnbuckle for adjusting the length of the brace, and means to fasten the lower end of the brace to the floor. The latter can consist of a continuous plank fastened to the floor on which the end of the

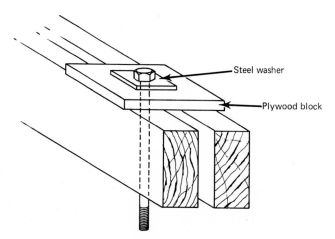

Steel washer

Plywood block

Fig. 2.10—Detail of the strongback shown in Fig. 2.9. The bolt shown can be a bolt screwed into an anchor or a she bolt screwed into a J-bolt hooked under a reinforcing bar.

brace rests against a block attached to the plank, or a piece of flat bar steel or flattened end of a pipe which can be bolted to the floor. Whatever method is used, it must be capable of withstanding any expected wind load (Fig. 2.11). On small jobs simple wood braces are used, but they are not the most economical in every case. For greater safety and speed, the top connection should be made before the panel is raised. The bottom connection can be made as soon as the panel is approximately in a vertical alignment, releasing the crane to be attached to the next panel while the adjustable braces bring the panel to final alignment.

To determine the length of brace required, the upper connection should be made to the panel at a point two-thirds of the distance from the floor line to the top of the panel, as shown in Fig.

Fig. 2.11—Panels have been erected and braces attached to hold them in place until the columns have been constructed. Note the three-wide pickup; the length of the middle cable is adjustable so the load can be equalized.

2.12. Using a 3-4-5 right triangle, the total length of brace can be computed:

Length of brace $= 2/3D \times 5/4 = 0.83D$
Distance from base of panel to floor anchor $= 0.5D$

Some building codes specify the wind load a panel must withstand during construction, usually 10 psf. Knee braces will be required in most instances and are necessary also for very tall panels (Fig. 2.12).

COLUMNS

Forms for columns are set in place after the panels have been erected and lined up. Forming costs can be minimized by using only a few forms and constructing the columns as the work progresses. This requires careful planning so the ready-mix trucks can be scheduled economically.

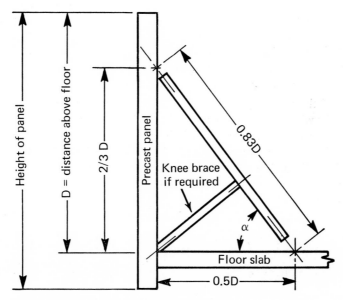

Fig. 2.12—In attaching a brace, consider the portion of the panel above the floor, which might not be the same as the height of the panel. The knee brace can be a piece of timber attached to the panel brace and bearing against the panel and floor.

Placing the concrete requires considerable care to avoid rock pockets and honeycomb. Columns are quite tall and made of small cross sections containing much reinforcing steel, and this makes concrete placing and consolidating difficult. Internal vibrators should be used for consolidating the concrete. Some contractors have developed a technique of attaching the end of the hose from the concrete pump to the bottom of the form and forcing the concrete into the form against the hydraulic head of the fresh concrete in the form. Others form two or three sides of the column and construct the column with shotcrete. When properly performed, this technique is satisfactory. See ACI "Recommended Practice for Shotcreting."[6]

Tilt-up panels can be erected so there is relatively slight movement between the panels and the cast-in-place columns, or they can be rigidly connected with deformed tie-bars extending through the edge of the panel into the column concrete. In areas of wide fluctuations in temperature, it is better to separate the panels from the columns so the panels can contract and expand without crushing or spalling.

Whether the panels are bonded to the columns or left free to move with contraction and expansion is a design decision. If bonded, the reinforcing steel tie-bars on the panel edges should be clean so the column concrete will bond properly. If unbonded, all horizontal steel is stopped just short of the panel edge, and smooth dowels are inserted. The dowels should be perpendicular to the edge of the panel and covered with grease, paper, or some type of bond breaker so they can move freely in the column concrete. In the latter case, the concrete of the panel that is to be in contact with the column concrete should be covered with a bond breaker. Further discussion of panel-to-column joinery will be found in Chapter 5.

3

HANDLING AND STORAGE

METHODS OF HANDLING and storing units have to be worked out for each plant, considering the types of units to be made. This is especially true of large or unusual-shaped units. Location and type of lifting inserts, the need for additional reinforcement to resist handling and lifting stresses, designation of support, and storage methods all must be fully engineered before production is commenced. Units must be handled and stored in accordance with these requirements. There is no standard method; the important criteria are safety and protection of the concrete.

It is always desirable to remove the casting from the form as early as permitted by the strength of the concrete, in order to make room for the next castings. Frequently the casting has to be moved to another part of the plant for further processing or finishing, an operation that may involve turning the unit in different positions so the workmen can have access to the several faces. Finally the unit is moved to the storage yard where it is stored in accordance with the previously designated method.

HANDLING

Rehandling of units is not only expensive but dangerous, increasing the chance of damage to the unit each time it is moved.

35

For example, a flat panel is likely to crack if it is laid flat after it has once been lifted off its casting surface. It is better to stand the panel on edge.

Actually, the "standard" methods of handling units are general methods. The great variety of sizes, weights, and shapes of units, together with the particular techniques for using many types of equipment developed in various plants, makes it difficult to conclude that one method or piece of equipment is better than any other. What is best under the conditions existing in one plant might not work at all in a different plant. If the method and equipment will remove the unit from its form safely and economically, move it as required, permit it to be turned to allow access to all sides for finishing or repair, and load it onto the delivery vehicle, then they are satisfactory, regardless of what might be done in another plant or for different types of precast units.

The storage area should be large enough so the units can be stored properly, with adequate room for lifting equipment and trucks to maneuver. A well-organized storage yard is clean, reasonably level, hard surfaced (but not necessarily paved), and with adequate provision for drainage of storm water and curing water. Foundations on which precast concrete is to be stored must be stabilized to prevent differential settlement that results in unequal loading or twisting of the elements. Units should not be stored on frozen ground without proper safeguards to prevent settlement when the ground thaws. Units must be raised above the ground surface so rebounding rainwater will not soil them (Fig. 3.1).

Pickup points are critical, and precast units should be lifted only at the designated points. When the units are stored, they must be similarly supported. Prestressed girders, beams, and other

Fig. 3.1—Safety and efficiency require a clean and orderly storage yard.

units must be supported only at the bearing points, or within a short distance designated by the structural engineer. They should never be supported even temporarily at any other point, and they should never be permitted to tip sideways. Most panel units are stored in a vertical or nearly vertical position, using two-point support. They should be stored in such a manner that each unit supports only its own weight, without any load imposed by other units. Points of contact between units must be provided with protective material to prevent breakage and staining (Fig. 3.2). Some special shapes can be stored flat.

Units that are stacked should be separated and supported on strips of wood or battens across the full width of each bearing point, as shown in Fig. 3.3. All battens must be in the same vertical plane within the specified maximum distance from the pickup point, sometimes specified not to exceed the depth of the unit; however, the shop drawings should be checked. This is especially

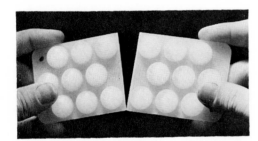

Fig. 3.2—Rope, timber, or special plastic pads such as the one shown can be used to separate units to prevent marring or breakage.

Fig. 3.3—Precast concrete elements can be stored flat if care is taken to support them on wood battens.

important for prestressed units. Miscellaneous items of equipment or short members should not be piled on top of a stack of units. In every case, care must be taken to protect the lifting devices from damage and keep them accessible. Care should be exercised in handling units to avoid impact and unusual loading, such as lateral loads, vibration, and distortion.

When units such as flat panels are stored in a vertical position, the first one should be placed on edge on protective material, then tilted back slightly against supports so it will be stable. Panels may be placed on both sides of the supports (see Fig. 3.4). Spacers for subsequent panels should be placed in line with the supports behind the first panel. Although the panels are tilted back slightly for stability, only a small part of the weight of the panel is transferred to the prior panel.

REPAIRS

Precast units should be inspected before the shipping date to allow time for proper repairs to be made. A final inspection is made just before shipment so any last-minute repairs can be made. Among the conditions that are unacceptable are the presence of rock pockets and honeycomb; sandy streaks resulting from leakage of grout or mortar at form joints; stains from iron or other sources; excessive surface voids or "bug holes" on smooth surfaces to be exposed; obvious fill planes or cold joints; irregularities in forms; offsets in adjacent form panels; irregularities in texture or color caused by errors in batching; segregation; use of wrong ma-

Fig. 3.4—Neat and safe vertical storage can be accomplished by inclining the units slightly against well-constructed buttresses. The units are separated by pads to prevent damage.

terials; inequalities in etching; sandblasting or other surface treatment; foreign material embedded in surface; rough, irregular, or ragged edges; shadow lines or "photographing" of reinforcement; excessive cracking; broken edges; and unmatched or crude patching. Rough and careless handling of units can cause unsightly damage, and final repairs may become necessary at the site. In some cases, certain inserts that were necessary for lifting the unit will be exposed after the unit has been erected. The inserts must be removed and their holes patched. The Architect/Engineer should approve the materials and technique to be used in this case.

One of the most troublesome problems encountered when patching any concrete is matching the color and texture of the original concrete. This problem is greatly magnified in precast concrete because of the variety of surfaces required and because most of the surfaces are of an architectural quality and will be exposed to view—usually very critical view—in the finished structure. For this reason it is mandatory that the workman doing this work be experienced and familiar with the procedures. He should be ingenious in developing special skills and techniques and have an eye for color and texture.

Patching should be done as soon as possible after the forms have been removed, either while the unit is still on the casting bed or later in the storage yard. If the units have been steam cured, the concrete probably will be lighter in color after it dries out than concrete cured at normal ambient temperatures. This must be considered when making the patch.

When patching gray concrete, use the same cement, sand, admixture, and water that were used in the original concrete, with from 10 to 30 percent white cement substituted for part of the gray cement. The mixes should be tested on small inconspicuous areas until a satisfactory match is obtained. Once the proper color has been achieved, the same proportions can be used for all concrete made with the same materials. Ingredients for the patching mixture should be proportioned by weight and the weights recorded, together with identification of the materials by brand or source, so the same patching mixture can be produced in the future.

White concrete patching, like gray, should be made with the same materials used in the original concrete. In a few cases, a small addition of titanium dioxide (not over 15 percent of the cement) might be desirable for extra whiteness. Here again, trials will have to be made and records kept so repairs can be properly made in the future.

Colored concrete is the most difficult to match and requires testing as previously described. If gray cement was used in the original concrete, a small amount of white cement will be necessary. The pigment should be added in the same proportion as was used in the concrete. For all practical purposes, consider the weight (in pounds) of color per sack or 100 lb of cement to be the percentage. For example, if the mix proportions call for 15 lb of color per cu yd of concrete using 6 sacks (384 lb) of cement, this is equivalent to 15/6, or $2\frac{1}{2}$ lb per sack of cement, which equals about $2\frac{1}{2}$ percent. Use this percentage in proportioning the patching mixture for this particular concrete. After tests have been made and the proper color match obtained, record the mix data for future use.

The first step in any repair is removal of all defective concrete such as rock pockets and honeycomb. This can be done with hand or power tools. If a pneumatic chipping gun is used, care must be exercised to avoid damage to the concrete, especially if the concrete has not developed much strength. The tool should not be permitted to strike and nick the prestressing strand in prestressed concrete.

Relatively deep cavities of small area, such as those resulting from cone bolts or form bolts, are best filled with a dry-pack mortar consisting of the previously determined mixture with just enough water so it will form a ball when squeezed gently in the hand. Too much water will result in shrinkage and consequent loosening of the patch; too little water will not make a sound patch. After the cavity has been cleaned of all loose material, unsound concrete, and oil, the mortar is tamped in layers about $\frac{1}{2}$ in. thick. For compaction and bonding between layers, tamping is best done by hammering on a hardwood stick. The surface of the patch should be finished to match the existing concrete. Even when matching a steel-formed or steel-troweled surface, a steel trowel should never be used on the patch, because it leaves a dark surface that is impossible to remove. Instead, lay a piece of smooth lumber against the mortar filling and strike it several times with a hammer. The dry-pack method can be used for making patches of appreciable area by building up the patch in layers.

For extensive repair of large areas of honeycomb or unconsolidated concrete it is necessary to replace the concrete. This method is used for repairs involving large and deep areas of more than a few square inches in area and 6 in. deep. Actually, any unit that is so bad that it requires concrete replacement is probably in such poor condition as to be unacceptable. Careful evaluation should be made before time and effort are expended in trying to make it acceptable, considering the ever present possibility that it will never be a first-quality product.

Repairs in horizontal surfaces can be made without forms, except where replacement of corners and edges is required. Sloping and vertical surfaces that were originally cast against forms will require forms to confine the repair concrete. Forms must be mortar-tight and must fit snugly against the old concrete to avoid loss of mortar or an offset around the perimeter of the patch. The old concrete should be moistened, then allowed to dry until no free water remains on the surface; then a $\frac{1}{8}$ in. coating of mortar of the same proportions and water content as the replacement concrete is applied by shotcreting or hand rubbing into the surface. Concrete placing follows immediately after the mortar coating. Concrete with a slump of 2 or 3 in. should be deposited in layers, each layer consolidated by vibration (using immersion vibrators if possible, otherwise by means of form vibration provided the form was constructed to withstand form vibration). Under carefully controlled conditions a small amount of powdered aluminum (2 or 3 grams per sack of cement) can be added to the concrete to partially compensate for shrinkage.

Pneumatically applied mortar or shotcrete is especially adaptable to thin areas of large extent, such as scaled areas. Preparation of the area must be as described in this section. Application is described in the ACI "Recommended Practice for Shotcreting."[6]

The mortar coating just mentioned can be classified as a bonding agent since its purpose is to promote bond between the concrete and patch. Epoxy resin compounds are also used for this purpose, applied to the concrete immediately ahead of the patching material. The resin must be applied to dry concrete and used in accordance with the manufacturer's instructions. Certain latex compounds such as polyvinyl acetate can be added to the fresh mortar or concrete as an admixture, serving to improve bond. However, some agencies do not permit their use in areas where moisture is apt to be present at any time in the future.

All patches require thorough curing. This may be done by keeping them continuously wet for 5 days, by the use of liquid curing compound, or by covering them tightly with waterproof paper or polyethylene. A wet pad of burlap or similar material held tightly against the patch with a piece of plywood is effective.

LIFTING EQUIPMENT

Cranes and lifting machines are as varied as plant layouts. One popular type is a rubber-tired, self-propelled, straddle machine (Fig. 3.5). These machines are made with inside clear widths ranging from 12 to 40 ft and heights from 12 to 40 ft, with wheel bases to suit the particular plant usage. Although large and seemingly awkward, these machines are constructed with 90 deg pivot steering so they can maneuver in the narrow aisles usually found in storage yards. Capacities up to 100,000 lb are available. Long girders can be handled by two machines in tandem.

The machine shown in Fig. 3.6 is a heavy-duty forklift with an extra wide frame to enable it to carry long cored slabs. Truck cranes (Fig. 3.7), locomotive cranes, and small hydraulic cranes,

Fig. 3.5—Straddle carriers are efficient machines for moving units about the yard and loading them onto vehicles for transportation to the job site. Hoist traverse, propulsion, and steering are powered by hydraulic motors that are supplied from either a gasoline engine or diesel-driven hydraulic pump.

Fig. 3.6—A well-designed special lifting device enables this forklift to handle fairly long cored floor units.

are also widely used. In some yards overhead bridge cranes and gantry cranes are used.

A type of small crane frequently used in yards and for erecting is the hydraulic model shown in Fig. 3.8. Mounted on a truck as shown in Figs. 3.8 and 3.9, the crane is easily maneuverable, yet the boom can be extended to make the crane useful for erecting. The capacity chart in Fig. 3.10, for a telescoping boom hydraulic crane with a rated capacity of 10 tons, shows the effect of boom length and elevation on the actual lifting capacity of the crane. This particular crane has a boom that extends to 75 ft.

Whether in the plant or on the job, equipment and rigging methods for handling precast concrete are pretty much the same. Additional information will be found in Chapter 6.

LIFTING HARDWARE

Handling of precast concrete is likely to impose loads on the concrete entirely different from the structural design loads. These lifting loads must be considered when designing the precast units. Handling of the units involves removing the unit from the mold or form, transporting to temporary yard storage, loading and transporting to the construction site, unloading, storage at the site (sometimes), and finally erection and attachment to the structure. Precast members can be handled as soon as the concrete develops

Fig. 3.7—Truck cranes are widely used in yards and on the job.

44

Fig. 3.8—Hydraulic cranes of relatively low capacity, being versatile and maneuverable, are used in many yards.

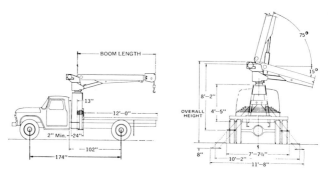

Fig. 3.9—The hydraulic crane shown in Fig. 3.8 can be easily mounted on a truck with a single rear axle capacity of 15,000 lb.

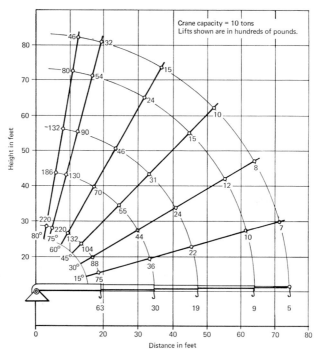

Fig. 3.10—Capacity charts are available showing the effect of boom length and angle of inclination on the actual lifting capacity.

sufficient strength. Prestressed members, either pretensioned or post-tensioned, can be handled immediately after transfer of stress to the concrete. However, units should be handled no more than absolutely necessary.

Depending on the size, weight, and type of unit, a number of lifting and handling techniques have been developed making use of various hardware items for attaching the rigging to the concrete. In some cases a unit can be lifted by merely slipping slings around it at appropriate places (Fig. 3.11). Usually, however, the use of slings is not practical because of interference with other parts of the structure or the introduction of unusual stresses in the concrete, so other means must be provided. This can be accomplished by embedding anchoring devices in the concrete when the unit is cast and attaching suitable lifting hardware when it is desired to move the casting.

A simple device, frequently used on prestressed girders and beams, is to embed several loops of prestressing strand in the concrete, leaving the loop exposed for attachment to the crane hook (Fig. 3.12). The exposed end of the loop should be located above the bearing of the girder, i.e., on the center line in the same vertical plane as the bearing.

Many special devices are available from manufacturers of concrete hardware. Whatever devices are used, their location in the unit must be carefully computed, taking into account the special loading that will be imposed on the concrete as a result of tilting, lifting, or moving the unit, including an allowance for impact. Impact allowance may be specified at some value between 50 to 100 percent of design load. Details and locations of lifting devices and handling devices should be shown on the shop drawings. As an example of lifting stresses, raising a tilt-up panel to a vertical position induces stresses in the concrete that exceed any loading that may be imposed on the panel after it has been installed in the building.

Any lifting device consists of two parts: (1) the anchorage element embedded in the precast concrete and (2) the attachment element which is attached to the anchorage to fasten lifting lines to the unit. To provide maximum strength, the anchorage should bear against the regular reinforcement. One of the simplest anchorage elements consists of some sort of spiral or threaded unit embedded in the concrete. This forms a "nut" into which

Fig. 3.11—Slings and chokers can be used for lifting many precast units, shown here attached to a prestressed bridge girder. Note the rubber and timber lagging under the chokers to protect the concrete. A tag line is attached to each end of the girder.

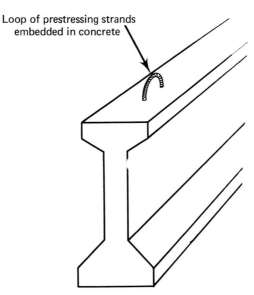

Loop of prestressing strands
embedded in concrete

Fig. 3.12—Scrap ends of prestressing strand can be embedded in the concrete to provide lifting eyes. Ends of the strands should be spread out in the concrete to provide bond so the strand will not pull out.

a bolt can be inserted. Special bolts can be used, or in some
anchors standard machine bolts are used. To increase the pullout
resistance of the anchor, a wire loop is welded to the coil (Fig.
3.13), thus increasing the depth of embedment. The loop may be
single or multiple, straight or flared. Some are designed with a
loop through which a short bar of reinforcing steel can be inserted.
From these basic elements scores of devices have been developed
by the manufacturers to fit almost every conceivable need that
might develop. Selection of the correct insert depends on a number of factors concerned with the type, weight, configuration,
thickness, and strength of the precast member, as well as personal
preference and indications on the shop drawings. The insert selection should be based on the manufacturer's recommendations
together with an engineering analysis of the proposed installation.
Dimensions and capacities shown in Fig. 3.13 are general and for
information only.

Inserts may be subject to direct tension loading, as occurs when
a spreader bar is used (Fig. 3.14), or in some cases when a single
line is used. Many conditions of loading, however, are not in di-

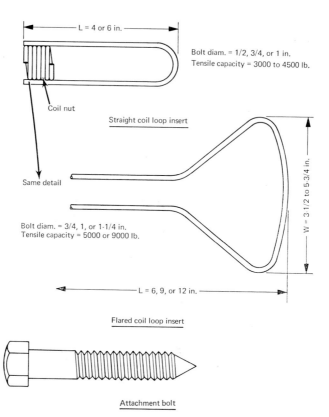

L = 4 or 6 in.

Bolt diam. = 1/2, 3/4, or 1 in.
Tensile capacity = 3000 to 4500 lb.

Coil nut

Straight coil loop insert

Same detail

Bolt diam. = 3/4, 1, or 1-1/4 in.
Tensile capacity = 5000 or 9000 lb.

W = 3-1/2 to 5-3/4 in.

L = 6, 9, or 12 in.

Flared coil loop insert

Attachment bolt

Fig. 3.13—A wire loop welded to the spiral wire "nut" provides anchorage in the concrete. The loop can be flared to provide greater capacity; a double flared loop doubles the capacity. Multiple loops provide even greater capacity.

Fig. 3.14—Spreader bars distribute the load on the rigging and enable lifts to be made with the inserts under direct tension.

rect tension and require a consideration of bending and shearing forces. In Fig. 3.15 a prestressed girder is being lifted by means of inserts at each end and without a spreader bar, a common method of handling precast concrete.

Fig. 3.15—A prestressed girder being lifted with bridle slings. Slings are attached to inserts at each end of the girder. Note the tag line.

Each insert carries a vertical reaction equal to ½L, in which L = total crane load or weight of the unit (Fig. 3.16). In addition, the insert must carry the horizontal component H of load L.

$$H = \frac{L}{2} \cot \beta$$

The tensile stress T in the sling depends on the value of L and the angle β that the sling makes with the precast unit.

$$T = \frac{L}{2 \sin \beta}$$

Obviously, the use of long slings is desirable to keep the values of H and T as low as possible.

Most inserts are so designed that the horizontal component H is applied at a short distance above the surface of the concrete; the insert must carry an additional vertical load, V, which is a tensile load comprising part of the couple that resists H. The value of V is computed from a consideration of d, the distance from the center line of the anchor bolt to the edge of the insert bearing

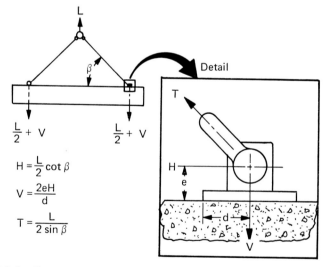

Fig. 3.16—Loadings on inserts and tension in the slings increase as the angle decreases.

plate; e, the distance from the face of the concrete to the point of application of the horizontal component H; and the magnitude of H.

$$V = \frac{2eH}{d}$$

Total tensile load on each anchor $= \dfrac{L}{2} + V$.

FAILURE OF CONCRETE INSERT

Depending on the relative actual strength of the insert and the concrete compared with stresses imposed by the loading, an insert under tensile loading can fail in one of three ways.

1. The entire insert might pull out of the concrete with little or no damage to the insert, leaving a small conical hole in the concrete. Usually the anchorage element of the insert (wire loops) pulls loose intact because of bond failure. A failure of this kind will occur when the insert is embedded too close to the surface where the concrete does not have adequate strength. This will also occur if a lift is attempted while the concrete has not developed the design strength, even though the anchor has been properly embedded.

2. If the insert is overloaded, it may fail by breaking the wire loops or legs, even when embedded in high-strength concrete. A small cone-shaped piece of concrete will be pulled out with part of the insert.

3. In some cases the entire insert pulls out of the concrete, taking with it a cone of concrete in which the insert is embedded. This usually occurs in low-strength concrete in which the strength of the insert is greater than the shearing strength of the concrete surrounding it.

To avoid failures like these, select an insert of adequate capacity for the intended lift. Most specifications require a design based on a total load equal to dead load plus 50 percent impact load. The insert must be embedded to a sufficient depth so the shear cone in the concrete will have sufficient area to resist the loading, and the concrete mixture must be proportioned to possess the necessary strength at the age it is desired to move the unit.

Bolts must be of the correct diameter and length, neither too short nor too long, and must be tightened securely to prevent bending. A bolt is too long if it has to be shimmed so it can be tightened against the surface.

The failure in Fig. 3.17 occurred when an attempt was made to rotate the precast unit before the concrete had attained sufficient strength to withstand the tensile load combined with a slight flexural load on the inserts which were located close to the edge of the member.

VACUUM LIFTING DEVICES

By making use of the principle that a device can be attached to any surface by creating a vacuum between the two, lifters have been developed for lifting precast concrete units. Vacuum lifters have been used for removing units from the forms and moving them about the storage yard and for erection. One advantage of vacuum lifters is the reduction in handling time; it takes only

Fig. 3.17—The inserts pulled out when an attempt was made to rotate the panel from horizontal to vertical.

a few seconds to attach or release the lifter. Also, the panel is not disfigured by holes for inserts that have to be patched later. It is usually possible to locate the lifter so as to minimize lifting stresses. In some cases, the lifter covers nearly the entire area of the panel. A lifting capacity of up to 340 lb per sq ft of gasketed plate is claimed with a safety factor of about 4. It is recommended that the foreman of the placing crew be responsible for releasing the vacuum, thus eliminating the possibility of the vacuum being released at the wrong time.

For the large panels found in precast work, it is standard practice to divide the vacuum area into subsections to provide improved pump efficiency. Each lifting unit has its own power supply and vacuum pump (Fig. 3.18). If the lifter is being used on

Fig. 3.18—Vacuum lifters come in a variety of sizes and capacities and are adaptable to a variety of precast units.

members that are rotated after removal from the truck, the power and vacuum units can be mounted on a pendulum suspension that keeps them upright as the panel, with the lifters, is tilted or rotated. A reservoir is built into each unit that provides a failsafe period of an hour or more in case of failure of the power or vacuum producing units.

RIGGING

Slings for handling precast concrete may be made of fiber rope, wire rope, or chain, the commonest being wire rope. Choker slings are occasionally used but must be used with care to avoid damaging the concrete by marring the surface or breaking corners and edges. Edges can be protected by the use of some type of guard, as shown in Fig. 3.19 which illustrates the use of a plastic chain guard. The lift being made in Fig. 3.11 was made with choker slings. Note the rubber and wood cable guards protecting the concrete.

Use of a spreader bar eliminates the problem of compensating for horizontal components on lifting devices and subjects the rope or chain to less tensile stress than the bridle arrangement. In using a bridle sling, remember that its working capacity is greatly reduced as the angle at which the lines intersect the concrete decreases. If the angle β in Fig. 3.16 is 90 deg, the capacity of the two lines is 100 percent; this capacity is negligibly affected for values of β between 90 and 75 deg. For angles smaller than 75 deg the sling capacity decreases so that

Fig. 3.19—Corner guards can be made of lumber, rubber, or (as shown here) plastic.

at β = 60 deg, capacity is 90 percent,
at β = 45 deg, capacity is 70 percent, and
at β = 30 deg, capacity is 50 percent.

These approximate values apply to either rope or chain slings.

Properly designed and manufactured end fittings for wire rope can develop the full working strength of the rope. The zinc socket is good for 100 percent of the rope strength; a thimble attached with clips will carry about 80 percent of the rope capacity; a thimble attached by splicing and seizing the wire, 100 percent; and an open wedge socket, 70 percent. Open wedge sockets should always be clipped as a safety measure.

Clips should be attached to the wire rope with the base of the clip against the line (long) end of the rope and the U-bolt bearing on the dead (short) end of the rope (Fig. 3.20). The first clip should be close to the thimble, and the others spaced equally about six rope diameters apart.

Hooks on rigging should be fitted with a safety latch (Fig. 3.21) which prevents the wire rope from slipping out of the hook. These latches, however, are not infallible and can be damaged so they become inoperative. If an attempt is made to fill the hook with

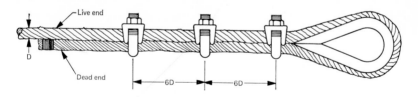

Rope dia.	Dia. of U-bolt	Approx. Wgt, lb	No. of clips for each rope end
1/4	3/8	0.29	2
3/8	7/16	0.46	2
1/2	1/2	0.73	3
3/4	5/8	1.46	3
1	3/4	2.66	4
1-1/4	7/8	4.63	5
1-1/2	7/8	5.48	6

Nuts on clips should be re-tightened after rope is in service and under load.

One additional clip should be used on high strength strands and rope with a wire core.

Fig. 3.20—Proper attachment of thimbles is essential for satisfactory performance of wire rope.

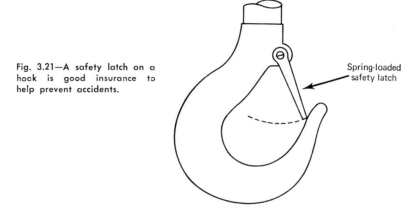

Fig. 3.21—A safety latch on a hook is good insurance to help prevent accidents.

Spring-loaded safety latch

too many passes of the rope, the latch can be damaged, bent, or forced open from below. Cases have been found in which the latch was wired back. Regular inspection will reveal deficiencies, which can then be corrected.

Blocks also must be inspected about every two weeks under continuous operation or every month if subject to intermittent service. Problems to look for include spreading of the hook, spreading of side plates, wear of the bearings resulting in loose sheaves, wear in the groove (including corrugations that cause rapid wear of the wire rope), and broken flanges.

Wire rope should be maintained in proper working condition, free of kinks and broken wires, properly lubricated, and of adequate capacity. Using a safety factor of 4, the safe lifting capacity of spreaders, slings, and trusses should be established and marked on the item. Any damaged equipment should not be used.

4

TRANSPORTATION

PRECAST MANUFACTURERS and carriers engaged in the specialized business of hauling precast and prestressed concrete units have developed various types of equipment for this purpose. A good example is the truck-trailer combination for hauling long prestressed girders. The units shown in Fig. 4.1, each weighing 60 tons, were transported over the highway under a special permit using a 44-wheel, 7-axle combination especially assembled for this purpose. This illustrates the problems that are sometimes confronted by the carriers. Long and heavy girders can be moved efficiently by rail, especially over long distances (Fig. 4.2).

LOADING THE VEHICLE

Loading of any type of unit on the truck or carrier must be done so as to provide adequate support and cushioning so blocking and tie-downs can minimize damage while the unit is in transit. Particular care is necessary to assure that flexing of the truck or trailer bed is not transmitted to the units. Units on trucks, rail cars, or barges must be supported as they were in the storage yard, with added bracing to assure that they remain in this loaded position without shifting or overturning. Adequate padding must be

Fig. 4.1—Large and heavy members can be transported with special equipment. These 60-ton units were successfully moved with the dolly arrangement shown.

Fig. 4.2—Long-distance hauling of very long units is best accomplished by rail. Note the lateral trussing consisting of two strands on each side of the girder. Anchorage of the strands is shown in Fig. 4.8.

inserted between chains, cables, or ropes and the members to prevent chipping or other damage, a precaution especially important on edges and corners. This padding can consist of timber blocks or lagging, rope mats, or plastic pads manufactured just for this purpose (Figs. 3.2 and 3.19). It should not stain the concrete either dry or wet.

Most precast panels can be supported on an A-frame on the bed of the truck, trailer, or rail car, to hold the panels in a nearly vertical position (as shown in Figs. 4.3 and 4.4), with the panels loaded in such a manner as to minimize the weight of one unit bearing on another. The weight must be supported on suitable blocking at the bottom edge of the member. Nonstaining padding should separate the panels from each other and from the load binders or other supporting and holding material. Some panels can be loaded flat in a horizontal position (Figs. 4.5 and 4.6). In this case, it may be desirable to use a three-point supporting system

Fig. 4.3—A center A-frame supports small flat panels loaded on each side. Panels should be loaded and unloaded alternately from opposite sides to prevent unbalancing the load.

Fig. 4.4—Several sizes of small panels being loaded on a trailer.

Fig. 4.5—With adequate spacers and lagging, panels can be hauled in a horizontal position.

Fig. 4.6—Prestressed cored floor slabs properly loaded on a trailer. Note the battens between slabs. Tie-downs are yet to be applied to the load.

to minimize the effect of racking or warping of the vehicle during transit.

Lifting and handling connections can be bolts or eyes screwed into inserts cast in the concrete of the precast unit. Heavy canvas slings or belts are sometimes used and, in those cases where they are acceptable, are satisfactory. They are particularly useful for lifting floor and roof slabs, which can be raised in a horizontal position, as shown in Fig. 4.7. Edges and corners of the slabs should be protected to prevent spalling. Slabs of this type can also be raised by means of loops of reinforcing steel or prestressing strand embedded so they project through the top surface of the concrete, acceptable only if a cast-in-place topping is to be placed on the precast slabs or if the loops can be burned off. Still another method is to provide inserts for lifting bolts in the top surface of the slab. This has the advantage of a smooth top surface after the insert holes have been patched subsequent to erection.

LONG MEMBERS

In spite of the problems associated with unusually large or heavy loads, most plants do not restrict the size and weight of mem-

Fig. 4.7—Web belt slings are useful for lifting certain types of units, shown here lifting a prestressed cored floor slab.

bers produced. The designer should consider hauling conditions, however, keeping in mind that large and heavy units may in some cases increase construction costs. Long members are specified for bridges and are appearing with greater frequency in buildings. The designer should not only consider the design of the structure but should also make an analysis of manufacturing, handling, transportation, and erection costs (including allowances for special equipment and permits) to determine the advisability of specifying large members. Rail transportation is frequently used.

Lateral trussing or bracing might be necessary to prevent flexing of long slender units. Tees are usually rigid enough to require no trussing; however, extremely long tees should be braced. One method that has been used successfully on long slender single tees is to attach short lengths of steel angle on both sides of the stem near the ends of the tee and a structural steel strut on each side at the midspan, with one or two stressing strands stressed between the angles and over the strut on each side. The strands are cut or burned off and the hardware removed when the tee is lifted off the carrier and placed in the structure. A similar method used on I-beams is to attach the strand through steel flat bars bearing against the ends of the girder. More than one strand may be required, depending on the length and cross section of the girder. The bridge girder shown in Fig. 4.2 is trussed with two strands on each side. End anchorage of the strands is shown in Fig. 4.8, which

Fig. 4.8—End details of the long girder on rail cars shown in Fig. 4.2. This prestressed bridge girder is supported on a swivel bolster under each bearing. The trussing strands are anchored in short lengths of steel angle bolted to the girder.

also shows how the girder is held down on a swivel bolster on the rail car during transportation. Sometimes a strongback can be attached to the unit.

Pole trailers (Fig. 4.9) are commonly used, with the precast unit serving as the "pole" connection between truck and trailer. In using this arrangement the "landing gear" of the trailer unit is lowered and the tractor is driven ahead a sufficient distance to suit the length of precast girder being hauled. Then the girder is landed on the bolsters and the trailer secured to the girder so the landing gear can be raised. Securing the front end of the girder to the bolster on the tractor makes the load ready to travel. Another system is a spread semitrailer in which a center beam can be lengthened as much as 60 ft, separating the rear wheels of the semitrailer from the front end which is attached to the tractor. The center beam or pole connects the two hauling units. This is especially desirable for flexible members such as piling (Fig. 4.10). A heavy 16-wheel, single-bolster rear dolly is shown in Fig. 4.11.

Standard practice when tying a member to the truck or trailer is to have a single tie-down cable from the vehicle bed up and over the member and down to the vehicle bed on the other side. The tie-down cable should be blocked up to clear the corners or edges of the concrete to prevent damage. This is especially im-

Fig. 4.9—A pole trailer in which the prestressed tee serves as pole between rear dolly and front dolly.

Fig. 4.10—A spread semitrailer, looking from the rear dolly toward the front. The telescoping center beam is in the closed position.

Fig. 4.11—Heavy-duty 16-wheel, two-axle dolly with one bolster. This long prestressed girder is trussed on the sides.

portant when tees are being hauled; there have been cases in which the tee flanges have been damaged, especially when hauling over rough ground.

The number and spacing of axles are determined by legal limitations on wheel loads. Heavy girders might require a three-axle trailer with a semitrailer and tractor at the front end. Many times these heavy girders must be loaded with considerable overhang at either or both ends of the vehicle. This imposes cantilever loads on the girder that were not considered in the design; these members are usually designed to be supported at the ends. Under these circumstances it is necessary for the precaster to provide additional steel to carry the tensile stresses induced by the overhang. There is also the possibility of an unusual moment resulting from whipping action of the cantilever overhang during hauling, and an allowance should be made for this. The precaster must confer with the hauler before the units are cast, in order that such special problems can be resolved early and proper means agreed on to assure safe and efficient handling and transport of the units.

Single bolsters are normally used and must be used on the tractor or lead trailer, and on the rear trailer if it is to be steered. The trailing dolly shown in Fig. 4.12 is a typical two-axle, single-bolster. Occasionally, double bolsters are used on the rear trailer,

Fig. 4.12—A two-axle trailing dolly with one bolster.

in which case the prestressed unit must be fully seated on the outer bolster at a distance not exceeding 3 ft or the depth of the member from the end, whichever is smaller. The inner bolster must be not more than 8 ft from the end of the member (Fig. 4.13). Double bolsters provide somewhat more stability for the load than single bolsters.

Rear-end steering equipment (Fig. 4.14) can be efficiently used for long members and is necessary for making short-radius turns. A common type is a three-axle dolly on which the front axle can be steered by various means, including one in which a workman manipulates a system of cables either from the front end of the rig or from the dolly itself. Another system consists of electric cable controls that operate hydraulic rams. A gasoline engine on the dolly furnishes power for the hydraulic system. The single bolster is situated between the two front axles of the dolly.

TRANSPORTING AND UNLOADING

Truck and trailer combinations must be selected so the two vehicles are matched. One cause of poor trailering is a mismatched truck and trailer. A truck may have the weight and power to pull

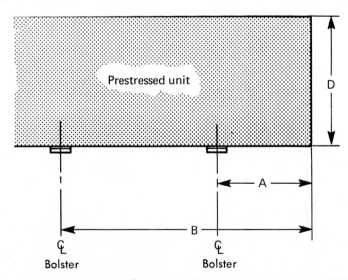

Fig. 4.13—The distance from the center line of the rear bolster on a double-bolster dolly to the end of the prestressed member (distance A) should not exceed "D" or 3 ft, whichever is smaller. Distance "B" from center line of inner bolster to end of girder should not be more than 8 ft.

Fig. 4.14—A rear-end steering dolly. Steering is accomplished by rigging that moves the front axle. The single bolster is situated between the front two axles.

a trailer through city streets, where speeds do not exceed 30 mph, but is not suitable for pulling the same trailer at high expressway speeds. A truck with an excessive rear overhang makes a poor towing vehicle, because the long overhang permits the trailer to weave and exert side forces on the truck which are dangerous to the load as well as to the vehicles. A trailer-towing truck should have the pintle hook as close to its rear axle as possible.

An improperly balanced load can also cause poor trailering. Maximum efficiency results if about 10–15 percent of the load is carried by the tractor at the pintle hitch.

Capacity of most vehicles is less at high speeds than at low speeds. The manufacturer's recommendation should be followed in this respect. These weight limitations apply to normal truck and trailer combinations. There are exceptions, such as the pole-type arrangement for long and heavy members, which normally operate at relatively slow highway speed under a special permit.

A significant item of cost is the density of the concrete in the precast members. From 20 to 33 percent more trips are required for normal weight concrete of 150 pcf density compared with lightweight concrete, assuming the same total weight per load. Lightweight concrete with a dry density of 110 pcf can be proportioned to have a 28-day compressive strength in excess of 5,000 psi. The cost of materials for this lightweight concrete is greater than that of normal weight concrete, and this additional cost must be equated against the possible benefits of fewer delivery trips, more units per load, and lighter hauling and handling equipment. Of course the structure must be designed for lightweight concrete.

Trucks and their loads must conform to laws governing their operation over the streets and roads involved. Especially with long or wide loads, there are likely to be limitations regarding the use of certain streets at certain times of day. It might be necessary to deliver such members over a specially selected route at night or on weekends. Laws governing weights and lengths of various truck and trailer combinations and their operation differ in different states and municipalities; the carrier should familiarize himself with all legal requirements that might apply to the movement of the units. Some states require that a vehicle precede and one follow the load, with signs warning of "long load" or "wide load." Other than legal requirements, it is necessary to study the route of travel to avoid narrow bridges, shallow underpasses, or any other obstructions that could interfere with free movement of the load.

Because of weather and road conditions, it is sometimes necessary to wrap or otherwise protect the units during transportation. This is especially important for members with architectural finishes that could be stained or discolored. Covering material must be nonstaining, such as polyethylene sheeting.

Upon arrival of the vehicle at the job site, the first operation is to remove all load binders, chains, and ropes confining the precast members. Then the exposed packing and padding are removed. Care should be taken to avoid damaging the concrete. Only one unit should be removed at a time, except for small units that might be grouped on pallets. Units should be removed from alternate sides of the vehicle to avoid unbalancing the load, and the remaining units should be braced to prevent slipping or tipping. Units on the outside or top of the load should be unloaded first. Never try to slide a member out from the center of the load.

SCHEDULING DELIVERIES

It is necessary that units be delivered to the job site in proper order for erection. Some jobs may have a storage area where a limited number of units can be stored, but it is usually best to lift the units directly off the truck onto the structure, except for numerous small ones. Members should be loaded in such order that they can be unloaded in proper sequence upon delivery, especially when units are to be erected directly from the truck without intermediate storage. Careful planning and scheduling are required to avoid unnecessary delays at the job site occasioned by delivery of the wrong unit or delivery at the wrong time. If a unit cannot be unloaded into temporary storage at the site, it probably means a return trip to the plant with the misassigned member.

Scheduling of deliveries is the responsibility of the erector, who must give adequate advance notice to the precaster and assure reasonable promptness in unloading. This scheduling depends on the erection plan developed in the early stages of the job and requires close coordination by the precaster, general contractor, erector, and delivering carrier. The erector should allow a certain degree of flexibility in the schedule to allow safe and economical positioning of the units on the truck when more than one unit is hauled per load, thus permitting the hauling of full loads; he should also allow for delays that are bound to occur occasionally through no fault of the manufacturer.

If units are to be stored on the job site, they should be covered with plastic sheeting, canvas, or waterproof paper to protect them from rain or an accumulation of dust and dirt. Handling and storing of precast concrete are covered in Chapter 3.

5

CONNECTIONS

Joints and connections referred to in this chapter are those used for connecting one precast member to another and to connect precast members to the structural frame of cast-in-place concrete, steel, or masonry. In performing this function, connections must transmit moments, shear, axial loads, and torsion (either singly or in combination) resulting from dead and live loads including service loads, earthquake and wind forces, handling and erection stresses, shrinkage and creep of concrete, temperature stresses, and certain other loadings resulting from construction and erection procedures. In addition, some loadings will be in compression, some in tension.

Connections can be continuous (in which the joint hardware, reinforcement, or the concrete itself takes the stresses) or discontinuous, such as a bearing support that obtains its stability from gravitational friction.

PROPERTIES

Some of the important properties of a successful connection are the following:

1. It must be structurally adequate to perform at both service load and ultimate load, taking into account all possible loading

conditions. The effect of camber and rotation as well as erection stresses should be considered. Camber may result in displacement of the assumed locations of the reactions, and restrained rotation will cause moments in the connections. Good engineering decrees that the concrete members fail before the connections, normally achieved by providing a safety factor in the connections 10 percent higher than in the adjacent members.

2. It must be compatible with the architecture of the structure, preferably not visible in the finished structure. If it must be exposed to view, it should be neat and unobtrusive, nonrusting and nonstaining, and watertight. Edges and corners should be chamfered and beveled.

3. It must accommodate both manufacturing tolerances and erection tolerances. Both of these tolerances must be considered when determining sizes of holes, sleeves, dowels, corbels, and bearings, as well as erection clearances.

4. It should be designed so that temporary bracing or connections can be made to hold the precast unit in place so the crane can be released as soon as possible. Tying up an expensive crane and crew for an extended time while the connection is welded, bolted, or otherwise completed is a needless expense.

5. It should be the most economical connection possible that fulfills the requirements of 1, 2, 3, and 4, considering all factors of precasting, handling, and erecting. This implies the use of standard manufactured items readily available in the market rather than specials.

DESIGN

Design of connections must be made by a competent engineer familiar with precast concrete. The recommendations of ACI-ASCE Committee 512 [7] should be used. The following paragraphs from the Committee 512 report are especially pertinent to the present discussion:

103—GENERAL CONSIDERATIONS

It is recommended that joints and connections occur at logical locations in the structure and, when practical, at points which may be most readily analyzed and easily reinforced. Precautions should be made to avoid connection and joint details that would result in stress concentrations and the resulting spalling or splitting of members at contact surfaces. Liberal chamfers, steel-edged corners, adequate reinforcement, and cushioning materials are a few of the means by which such stress concentrations may be avoided or provided for.

The strength of a partially completed or completed structure should be governed by the strength of the structural members rather than by the strength of the connections; the connection should not be the weak link in the structure.

201—LOADING CONDITIONS

Loading conditions to be considered in the design of joints and connections are service loads including wind and earthquake forces; volume changes due to shrinkage, creep, and temperature change; erection loads; and loading encountered in stripping forms, shoring and removal of shores, storage, and transportation of members. Proper attention should be given to loads and the resulting stresses peculiar to the sequence of erection. Typical examples of construction in which the sequence and manner of erection affect the loading and stresses in the member are possible eccentric loading due to the erection of members on one side only of a member, installation of composite concrete toppings on shored or unshored slabs or beams, and continuity moment connections over supports. All significant combinations of loading should be considered, and the joints and connections should be designed for loadings consistent with these possible combinations of loading. For loadings other than those peculiar to precast concrete contruction (decentering, handling, storage, and erection loads), loadings and load distributions as outlined in ACI 318-71[8] should be the minimum considered.

If it is not practical to provide for all possible temporary loading conditions which could occur during erection, special erection procedures may be warranted. If so, complete erection instructions should be included in the plans and specifications which become part of the erection contract documents. Loading sequences, connection sequences, and if necessary shoring or guying schedules should be clearly outlined. The disposition and strength of shoring should be stated and approved prior to construction.

Drying shrinkage of concrete may have to be considered in designing connections if it is expected that precast members will be erected before the units have achieved their final equilibrium moisture content. Units that have air-dried for about a month can be considered to have developed most of their potential drying shrinkage. If the units are erected at the age of a week or so, the connections can be designed to accommodate the remaining shrinkage, or final tightening of the connections to restrain the member can be delayed.

Similarly, it may be necessary to allow for temperature variations which cause changes in the length of a precast member. Under a temperature change of 50 F, a member 100 ft long will change length about ⅜ in. |0 m|⇂⌐   ʒ𝑣 m⌐

The Architect/Engineer should be familiar with precasting and erection methods to enable him to detail the connections in accordance with standard designs. He must consider and evaluate the combinations of axial loads, shear, flexure, torsion, and moments that will act on the joint. Simplicity is desirable, keeping to a minimum the number of bolts, nuts, welds, and other pieces of hardware and permitting final adjustment after erection with the least number of operations.

Usually, inserts for attaching window frames, conduit, and interior partitions are not cast in the concrete; it is more economical to make these connections after erection of the units. Large holes (10 or 12 in. diameter or square) are cast into the units; small holes can be drilled by the trades involved. Care should be exercised in using drills and powder-actuated inserts to avoid striking and damaging prestressing tendons or reinforcing and to keep a reasonable distance from edges of the concrete that might be spalled or otherwise damaged.

Connections should be designed and constructed so that connection can be made under the most unfavorable combination of manufacturing and erection tolerances, including those of cast-in-place concrete, requiring that consideration be given to the casting tolerances of the precaster; in addition the joint must lend itself to adjustment during erection in the field to meet job erection conditions. The joint should be designed so it is capable of transferring all loads imposed on it, laterally and vertically, with a known factor of safety, and should not undergo unanticipated displacement or rotation that might cause high local stresses. Neoprene bearing pads, shims, wedges, and dry-pack mortar are used.

Welding of connections should be done in accordance with recommendations of the American Welding Society.[9] Weldability of components of the joint should be determined beforehand. For example, reinforcing steel is harder to weld than A-36 structural steel; hence it is desirable to use structural angles, plates, channels, and similar shapes as much as possible for welded joints. Many engineers disagree with the practice of welding a bearing plate or similar item to a reinforcing bar at a bend in the bar, because of the danger of the bar cracking or breaking at the weld. For this reason, mild steel anchor bars should be used, or the weld should be made on a straight portion of the reinforcing bar if possible. During welding it is necessary to protect adjacent concrete surfaces from damage resulting from heat that can cause spalling or smoke staining. A weld once made is final; there are no subsequent adjustments. Figure 5.1 shows a welded connection of a Mo-Sai mullion. The welder in Fig. 5.2 is welding the dowels to the structural pipe column that forms the center of the mullion.

Concrete cover for fire protection of connections, where required, should be at least as thick as the concrete cover required for the members.

Bearing pads should be used where precast members bear on masonry walls, with the bearing raised slightly so rotation under load will not cause the member to bear on the edge of the masonry. A soft elastomer is preferred to a steel plate. Rubber polymer asbestos pads are often used. The following bearing values have been used and are suggested:

    a. Allowable bearing stress on precast unit based on actual
       bearing area .... $0.25\ f_c'$
    b. Allowable bearing stress on supporting concrete in wall,
       beam, or lintel block, based on actual bearing area .... $0.30\ f_c'$
    c. Allowable uniform compressive stress on Grade A solid ma-

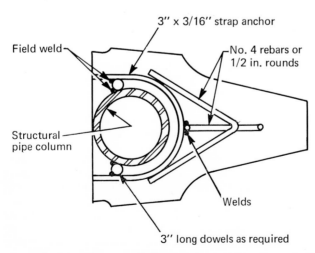

Fig. 5.1—A simple but effective welded connection attaches the embedded strap anchor to the steel pipe column.

Fig. 5.2—The welder is welding the strap anchor connection of the Mo-Sai precast panel illustrated in Fig. 5.1.

sonry units (ASTM C 145) set in Type M (A1) mortar (ASTM C 476) .... 175 psi

d. Allowable uniform compressive stress on Grade A hollow masonry units (ASTM C 90) set in Type M (A1) mortar ..... 85 psi

e. Allowable concentrated compressive stress on Grade A solid masonry units set in Type M (A1) mortar .... 260 psi

With respect to certain connections in areas where seismic (earthquake) conditions prevail, the Uniform Building Code[10] provides:

Exterior elements. Precast, nonbearing, nonshear wall panels or other elements which are attached to or enclose the exterior shall accommodate movements of the structure resulting from lateral forces or temperature changes. The concrete panels or other elements shall be supported by means of cast-in-place concrete or by mechanical fasteners in accordance with the following provisions.

A. Connections and panel joints shall allow for a relative movement between stories of not less than two times story drift caused by wind or seismic forces, or ¼ in., whichever is greater.

B. Connections shall have sufficient ductility and rotation capacity so as to prevent fracture of the concrete or brittle failures at or near welds. Inserts in concrete shall be attached to or hooked around reinforcing steel, or otherwise terminated so as to effectively transfer forces to the reinforcing steel.

C. Connections to permit movement in the plane of the panel for story drift may be properly designed sliding connections using slotted or oversize holes or may be connections which permit movement by bending of steel.

TYPES

It would be impossible to show all possible connections that have been used. These designs are suggestions to show the general types of connections that can be made and have been used successfully on some jobs. It should be emphasized that these are typical; the design and selection of connections should be made by a structural engineer familiar with this type of work, designing the connections to suit the unique requirements of the job.

In a precast rigid frame, connections between components can be made by means of scarf connections, as shown in Fig. 5.3. By locating a properly designed joint near the point of contraflexure, the effect on the frame should be negligible. Scarf connections are joined by means of bolts through the members. Bolts may be of mild steel or, if they are to be prestressed, of high-strength steel. Cushioning material can be mortar or, to speed erection, dry material such as asbestos cloth. Bitumen impregnated paper has the undesirable tendency of lubricating the joint.

Details of methods of joining precast columns to a cast-in-place

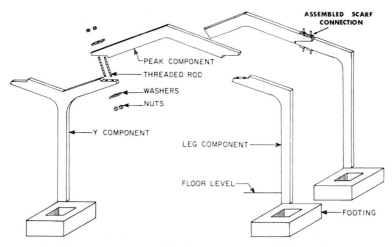

Fig. 5.3—Scarf connections are used for joining precast rigid frame elements.

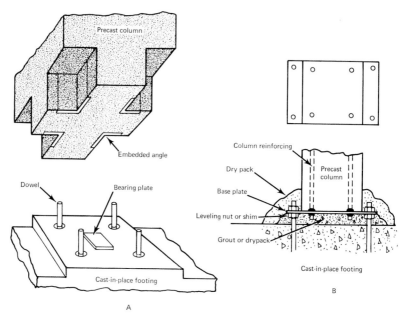

Fig. 5.4—Both of these details are used for attaching the column to the cast-in-place concrete.

base are shown in Fig. 5.4. Some contractors, instead of welding the base plate to the vertical column reinforcement as shown in Fig. 5.4,[8] attach the plate to welding studs which are embedded in the column concrete. In any of these connections the column is lowered into place on the preset base pad or nuts and guyed so the crane can be released; then the nuts are tightened or the weld is made. These connections provide immediate stability, and the bolted connection especially permits easy adjustment of the column for elevation and plumb. Dry-pack mortar is tamped into place as soon as the column is adjusted in place, with great care taken to fill the space below the baseplate completely. Finally, dry-pack fireproofing is packed around the joint.

A successful detail that has been used in many cases of tees bearing on walls or corbels similar to that shown in Fig. 5.5 consists of a small steel insert plate cast into the bottom of the stem on the tee. After the tee has been erected, this plate is welded to a bearing plate that in turn rests on an elastomeric pad on the concrete. Anchor bolts, attached to inserts in the cast-in-place concrete, pass through slotted holes in the bearing plate, one on each side of the

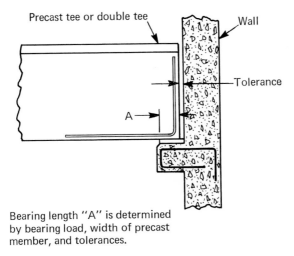

Bearing length "A" is determined
by bearing load, width of precast
member, and tolerances.

Fig. 5.5—Tee girders can rest on a corbel cast in the wall. Connection can be made by means of welded plates or embedded bolts through slotted holes in the bearing plates (see Fig. 5.6). Note the bevel on the edge of the corbel.

stem of the tee. The slots being aligned parallel to the longitudinal axis of the tee permit horizontal movement at the joint (Fig. 5.6).

A common girder- or beam-to-column connection (Fig. 5.7) shows two girders resting on an interior column. This connection can also be used for a single girder on an exterior column. By providing haunches or corbels on the column, the joint is adaptable to a multistory column. Bearing plates are fixed in the column concrete and insert plates in the beam concrete. Upon erection of the girder, a shim plate is inserted between the insert and bearing plates. If a steel shim plate is used, it can be welded to the insert and bearing plates.

A connection to serve the same purpose can be made with stubs of steel beams built into the column. The beam stubs projecting from the column serve as brackets on which the girders rest. A connection of this type is quite economical and easy to make.

Another successful beam-to-column connection is shown in Fig. 5.8. Called a knife connection by its developer,[11] it was developed to avoid corbels and the lateral clearance requirements of notches. The two stubs projecting from the face of the column are the ends of the anchorage reinforcing bars for the negative moment steel (Item 8) in the beam. These stubs do not interfere with the beam blade (Item 2) when the beam is lowered into position, the

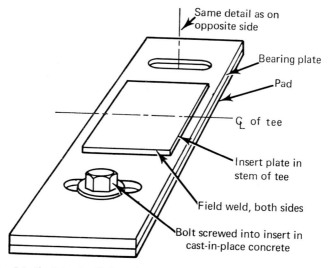

Same detail as on opposite side

Bearing plate

Pad

$\mathcal{C}_L$ of tee

Insert plate in stem of tee

Field weld, both sides

Bolt screwed into insert in cast-in-place concrete

Fig. 5.6—The joint detail shows how the bearing in Fig. 5.5 can be finalized.

beam blade sliding between the column sheath plates (Item 1). Alternatively, the beam can be raised into position. The erection bolts are now inserted and the crane released. Holes in one end of the beam, having been punched undersize, are reamed to absorb tolerances, and the structural bolts are installed. The negative moment steel is now set, the floor slabs are placed, and both beam and floor slab negative moment continuity welds are made. Finally, the ends are dry-packed and fill concrete is placed.

The sections illustrated in Fig. 5.9 show channel slabs resting on the beam, together with reinforcing steel. As shown in the figure, top steel from the channel slabs, projecting into the space between abutting slabs which is later filled with cast-in-place concrete, are welded to provide continuity after the beam negative steel has been welded.

Some contractors modify this procedure by elevating the far end of one member slightly, welding the connection, then lowering the unit, thus stressing the steel to more efficiently pick up the negative moment.

A method of providing for shear in a channel slab diaphragm is shown in Fig. 5.10. When concrete is placed in the space between the slabs, it fills the matching recesses, thus forming shear keys. Restraint provided by the beams keeps the slabs from moving apart. This is necessary to preserve the integrity of the joint.

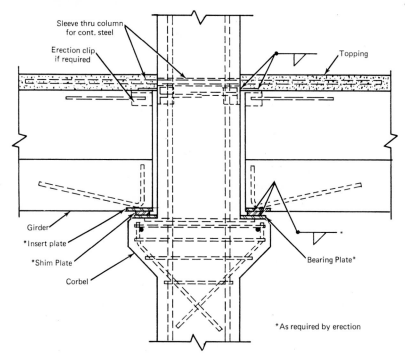

Sleeve thru column
for cont. steel

Erection clip
if required

Topping

Girder

*Insert plate

*Shim Plate

Bearing Plate*

Corbel

*As required by erection

Fig. 5.7—This sketch shows one possible joint at a girder to multistory column. Connection development in this detail, as in Fig. 5.5, is accomplished with welds or bolts. The anchor bars shown welded to the insert plates should be of mild steel, since a weld cn a bent reinforcing bar is likely to be a point of weakness.

A means of connecting the flanges of the tees, if it becomes necessary to provide continuity between precast tees, is shown in Fig. 5.11. Size and spacing of the connections must be determined for each installation. The steel angles are usually about 6-in. lengths of $1\frac{1}{2}$ x $1\frac{1}{2}$ x $\frac{1}{4}$ angle welded to steel anchors embedded in the concrete. Other flange connections are shown in Figs. 5.12 and 5.13. The detail shown in Fig. 5.12 is economical and simple but requires care in aligning inserts in adjacent members. It can be used where there is no structural topping slab to transfer diaphragm shear between tees.

Attachment of precast tees to steel and concrete girders is illustrated in Fig. 5.14. Note that the steel girder is a built-up section with a large lower flange that provides support for the tees when they are lowered into place. The concrete inverted tee girder is usually a precast, prestressed member. Several possibilities of

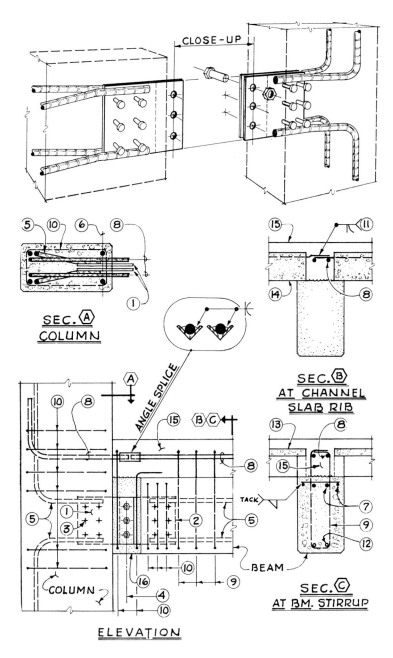

CLOSE-UP

SEC. Ⓐ
COLUMN

SEC. Ⓑ
AT CHANNEL
SLAB RIB

ANGLE SPLICE

TACK

BEAM

COLUMN

SEC. Ⓒ
AT BM. STIRRUP

ELEVATION

1. Sheath plates
2. Knife plate
3. Headed studs
4. Bolts
5. Anchor bars
6. Column rebar
7. Crack control and edge rebar
8. Negative moment rebar
9. Stirrups
10. Confinement hoops
11. Channel slab continuity splice
12. Prestress strand
13. Channel slab
14. Channel slab rib
15. Topping and cast-in-place concrete
16. Drypack

Fig. 5.8—Details of knife connection for the beam-to-column connection.

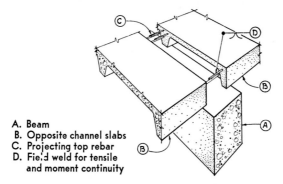

A. Beam
B. Opposite channel slabs
C. Projecting top rebar
D. Field weld for tensile
   and moment continuity

Fig. 5.9—Welding of reinforcement for continuity of channel slabs across a beam.

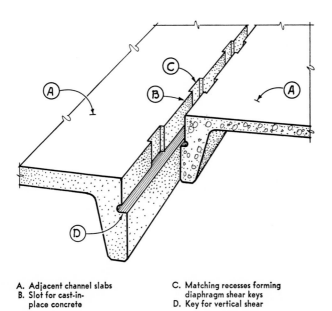

A. Adjacent channel slabs
B. Slot for cast-in-
   place concrete

C. Matching recesses forming
   diaphragm shear keys
D. Key for vertical shear

Fig. 5.10—Shear in the channel slab diaphragm can be provided by designing keys
for the cast-in-place concrete.

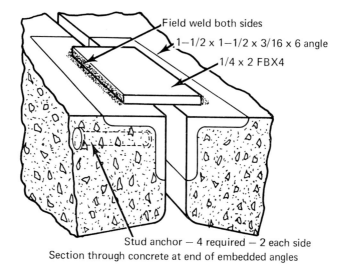

Field weld both sides

1–1/2 x 1–1/2 x 3/16 x 6 angle

1/4 x 2 FBX4

Stud anchor — 4 required — 2 each side

Section through concrete at end of embedded angles

Fig. 5.11—A simple method of providing continuity between precast tees is to cast short lengths of steel angle in the edge of the flanges. These are subsequently tied together by means of steel flat bars welded on the top.

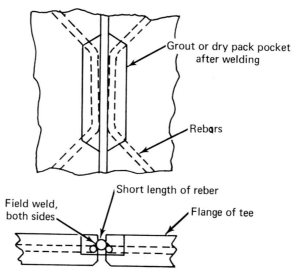

Grout or dry pack pocket after welding

Rebars

Short length of reber

Field weld, both sides

Flange of tee

Fig. 5.12—An economical and simple connection for tee flanges where there is no topping slab.

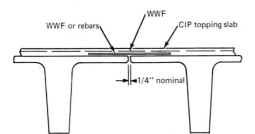

WWF

WWF or rebars

CIP topping slab

1/4" nominal

Fig. 5.13—Continuity can be accomplished with the cast-in-place topping slab, with extra reinforcing over the joint between the tees.

joint development are shown in Fig. 5.14. It is important to note that torsion can develop if tees are on one side only of the girder. To compensate for this, tees should be erected alternately on opposite sides of the girder.

In joining precast wall panels to columns in tilt-up construction, for example, whether to bond the wall unit to the column seems to depend mainly on geographical location. In areas governed by seismic codes it is common practice to bond the panel to the column by extending the horizontal panel steel far enough into the column to develop bond. Most codes require that half of the horizontal steel must be continuous for the entire length of the wall. The objection to this system is the danger of cracking. Many tilt-up buildings have suffered serious spalling and cracking where the panels join the columns as a result of tensile stresses induced by temperature changes. For this reason, many designers will free the panels so they can contract and expand independent of the columns, especially in areas where earthquake loading is not a problem and a wide range of temperatures exists (see also the discussion in Chapter 2). A typical connection of a precast panel to a cast-in-place column is illustrated in Fig. 5.15, showing the use of dowels wrapped in felt to allow movement. The column can be constructed by normal cast-in-place techniques or by shotcreting; forming by the latter method is simpler. Panels may or may not have the offset shown in Fig. 5.15.

Weld plates are a standard method of joining panel to column, as shown in Fig. 5.16. Weld plates can be spaced about 4 ft apart unless code or design requirements call for a different spacing. After the column has been erected and the welds are completed, the weld pockets on the sides of the column are dry-packed. The vertical diamond-shaped void between the panels is then grouted.

In making a connection to a steel column, the detail illustrated in Fig. 5.17 has been found to be satisfactory.[12] Again, spacing of

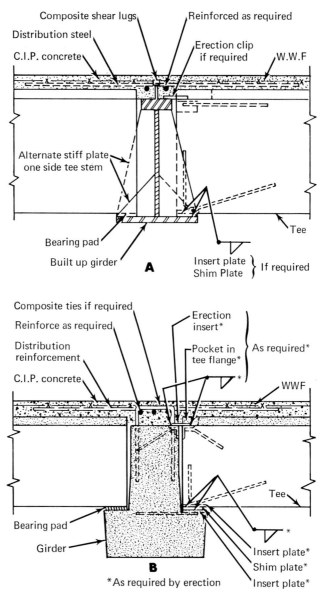

Composite shear lugs
Distribution steel
C.I.P. concrete
Reinforced as required
Erection clip
if required
W.W.F
Alternate stiff plate
one side tee stem
Bearing pad
Built up girder
A
Tee
Insert plate
Shim Plate } If required

Composite ties if required
Reinforce as required
Distribution
reinforcement
C.I.P. concrete
Erection
insert*
Pocket in
tee flange* } As required*
WWF
Bearing pad
Girder
B
*As required by erection
Tee
Insert plate*
Shim plate*
Insert plate*

Fig. 5.14—Attachment of prestressed tee to concrete and to steel girder. See Fig. 5.7 regarding welding anchors to insert plate.

88

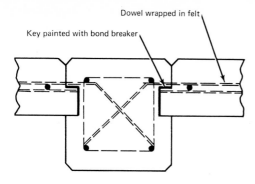

Key painted with bond breaker

Dowel wrapped in felt

Fig. 5.15—Connection of precast panel to cast-in-place column, designed to permit relative movement between the panels and the column.

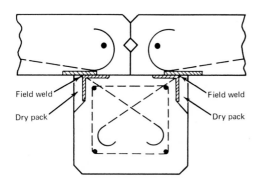

Field weld

Dry pack

Field weld

Dry pack

Fig. 5.16—A rigid connection between column and panels is provided by weld plates.

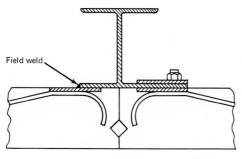

Field weld

Fig. 5.17—Either welded or bolted, this detail is satisfactory. The welded connection does not provide for any movement; some movement can be accommodated with the bolted connection.

the weld plates can be on 4-ft centers. Horizontal movement of the panel to prevent cracking can be accomplished by using a filler plate and bearing plate on the flange. This detail cannot be used where a fire rating is required, because there is no concrete or mortar covering over the steel.

Where panels are joined together, as at the end of a building without columns, similar joinery can be provided. The detail shown in Fig. 5.18 can be formed with offsets in the panel (as drawn) or with straight sides and will provide a 4-hr fire rating. This detail is similar to that in Fig. 5.15, with a 12-in. cast-in-place wall section substituted for the column. Similar to the column joinery in Fig. 5.16, the connection between panels can be made with weld plates as in Fig. 5.19. This joint does not have a fire rating.

A number of connections are illustrated in the booklet "Mo-Sai Design Details,[13]* showing attachment of many precast units to structural frames of different types. A few of these are reproduced here. As with all the suggested connections, the user is cautioned that these are guides only; each connection must be individually designed by a competent engineer to suit the requirements of the structure under consideration. Figure 5.20 shows a relatively simple

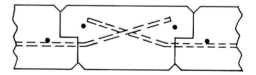

Fig. 5.18—This joinery can provide a rigid joint if panel reinforcing bars are extended into the column. If coated dowels are cast in the panels to extend into the column, movement is accommodated.

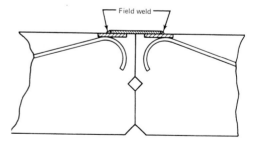

Fig. 5.19—A rigid connection between panels without a column can be provided by this detail.

---

* Mo-Sai is a precast architectural concrete with exposed aggregate surfaces manufactured under license of the Mo-Sai Institute. Mo-Sai is used as a structural, windowwall, curtain wall, flat panel, or decorative feature including sculptured forms. It is reinforced and may be pretensioned or post-tensioned.

method of attaching flat panels to a concrete frame by the use of bolted clip angles with a small T-column at vertical panel joints. Another connection, this time to a steel frame, is shown in Fig. 5.21; the same connection to concrete framing members is shown in Fig. 5.22. There are several possible variations of anchorages for these connections depending on the type of hardware selected (Fig. 5.23). For connecting precast panels to masonry wall construction, the detail shown in Fig. 5.24 can be used. Similar anchorages can be used when the backup is brick masonry, spacing the ties to fit into the

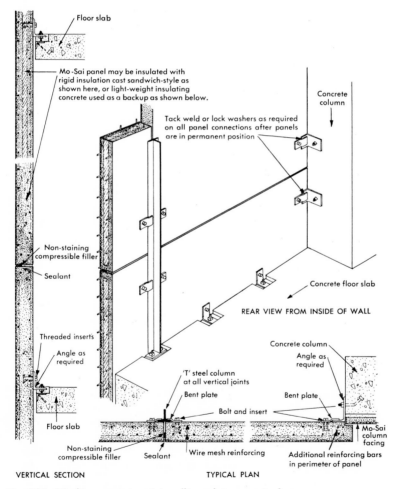

Fig. 5.20—Attaching precast curtainwall panel to concrete frame.

mortar joints between the bricks. Joinery of a precast panel to a concrete wall can be accomplished as illustrated in Figs. 5.25 and 5.26. The detail of Fig. 5.25 can be adapted to concrete masonry by using a threaded bent rod passing through a hole in the masonry and embedded in grout in the block cavity.

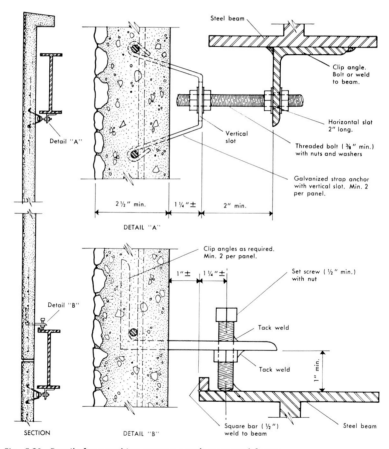

Fig. 5.21—Details for attaching precast panels to a steel frame.

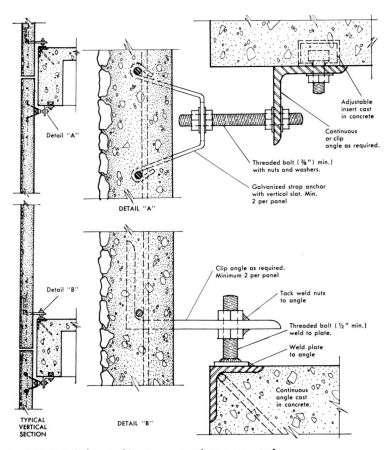

Detail "A"

DETAIL "A"

Adjustable
insert cast
in concrete

Continuous
or clip
angle as required.

Threaded bolt (⅜″) min.)
with nuts and washers.

Galvanized strap anchor
with vertical slot. Min.
2 per panel

Detail "B"

DETAIL "B"

TYPICAL
VERTICAL
SECTION

Clip angle as required.
Minimum 2 per panel

Tack weld nuts
to angle

Threaded bolt (½″ min.)
weld to plate.

Weld plate
to angle

Continuous
angle cast
in concrete.

Fig. 5.22—Details for attaching precast panels to a concrete frame.

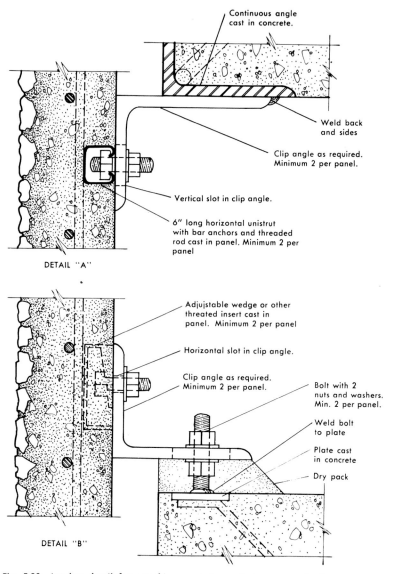

Continuous angle
cast in concrete.

Weld back
and sides

Clip angle as required.
Minimum 2 per panel.

Vertical slot in clip angle.

6" long horizontal unistrut
with bar anchors and threaded
rod cast in panel. Minimum 2 per
panel

DETAIL "A"

Adjustable wedge or other
threated insert cast in
panel. Minimum 2 per panel

Horizontal slot in clip angle.

Clip angle as required.
Minimum 2 per panel.

Bolt with 2
nuts and washers.
Min. 2 per panel.

Weld bolt
to plate

Plate cast
in concrete

Dry pack

DETAIL "B"

Fig. 5.23—Another detail for attaching precast panels to a concrete frame.

94

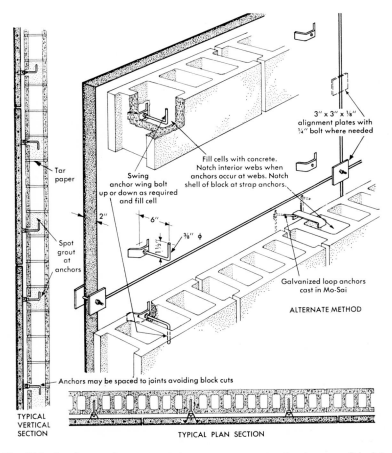

3" x 3" x ⅛"
alignment plates with
¼" bolt where needed

Tar
paper

Fill cells with concrete.
Notch interior webs when
anchors occur at webs. Notch
shell of block at strap anchors.

Swing
anchor wing bolt
up or down as required
and fill cell

2"

6"

⅜" φ

1½"

Spot
grout
at
anchors

Galvanized loop anchors
cast in Mo-Sai

ALTERNATE METHOD

Anchors may be spaced to joints avoiding block cuts

TYPICAL
VERTICAL
SECTION

TYPICAL PLAN SECTION

Fig. 5.24—Attachment of precast panels to masonry construction is accomplished by means of special anchors and clips.

95

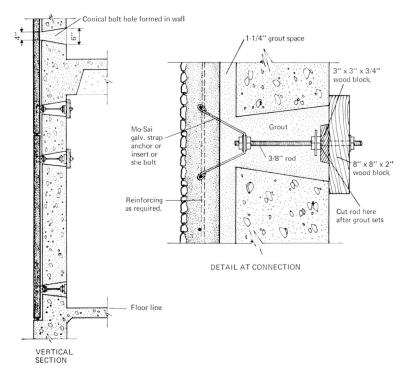

Conical bolt hole formed in wall

4"

6"

1-1/4" grout space

3" x 3" x 3/4" wood block

Mo-Sai galv. strap anchor or insert or she bolt

Grout

3/8" rod

8" x 8" x 2" wood block

Reinforcing as required.

Cut rod here after grout sets

DETAIL AT CONNECTION

Floor line

VERTICAL SECTION

Fig. 5.25—Precast curtainwalls can be attached to a concrete wall with grouted anchors. A grout space should be left between the panel and the cast-in-place concrete.

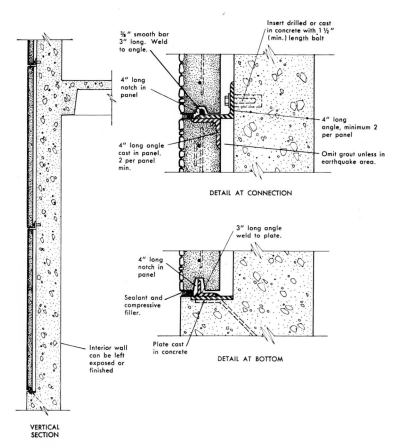

VERTICAL SECTION

⅜" smooth bar 3" long. Weld to angle.

4" long notch in panel

4" long angle cast in panel. 2 per panel min.

Insert drilled or cast in concrete with 1½" (min.) length bolt

4" long angle, minimum 2 per panel

Omit grout unless in earthquake area.

DETAIL AT CONNECTION

3" long angle weld to plate.

4" long notch in panel

Sealant and compressive filler.

Interior wall can be left exposed or finished

Plate cast in concrete

DETAIL AT BOTTOM

Fig. 5.26—Embedded anchors and angles serve as attachments of precast panel to cast-in-place structural concrete.

6
ERECTION

PREPARATION

PRIOR TO STARTING ERECTION the manufacturer, erector, and general contractor should check all job site conditions that might affect erection at any time.

The general contractor is responsible for providing (1) access to the structure, (2) unobstructed clearance around the building so the erection operations can proceed, including adequate areas for hoisting equipment of the erector, (3) access to windows and floor areas, and (4) bench marks and building lines throughout the building, as necessary.

If, during erection, errors or discrepancies are discovered that might affect installation of precast concrete, the erector should immediately stop work in the area and notify the general contractor. Erection should not be resumed until the error has been corrected and the general contractor has notified the erector to continue.

GENERAL

Erection includes removing the units from the delivery vehicle or onsite storage, rotating to the correct attitude, raising to the required elevation, placing in position on the building frame, adjusting, connecting, and caulking. In some installations temporary bracing is necessary

At the time of fabrication, the unit will have been clearly marked with the date it was made, an identifying number, a code number to indicate its position in the structure, and if necessary a marking to indicate the top of the unit. Standard off-the-shelf units should be further identified as to catalog number and certain design data. Many fabricators also show the weight of the member.

The shop or erection drawings should show the sequence of erection of the units. This sequence is based on a consideration of the loading on the building frame and the previously erected members, tolerances, and appurtenances to be attached. This sequence must be followed, unless the Architect/Engineer gives his approval of any proposed variations. At the end of each day the work should be properly secured to protect the unfinished structure from damage by high wind, rain, snow, vandalism, or any other cause. Steps should be taken during cold weather to protect holes and inserts from damage by water freezing in them. As the units are erected, they should be protected from damage and staining resulting from accidental impact, grouting, concrete placing, painting, or caulking when these operations are in progress.

Any turning or rotation of a unit should be done while it is suspended in the air on the erection lines, not on the ground or truck. A unit being lifted with a single line attached to one screwed insert should be guided with a tag line to avoid any possibility of the unit turning and unscrewing the insert.

The erector must exercise care in installing the unit to avoid any excessive loading of the unit itself, the building frame, or the connections, keeping in mind that during erection of precast concrete, the structure may at times be in an unstable condition. The members must be accurately positioned after installation and must be situated within the specified tolerances. All temporary handling and lifting devices should be removed as soon as possible. Initial fastening of the unit should be done as rapidly as possible so as to release the crane for other work.

As pointed out previously, precast units should be identified by a system that will show the final location of each unit in the completed building. A record should be kept by the erecting supervisor, noting on the erection plans the actual location of each unit placed, including date of erection.

Heavy members can conveniently be handled with two cranes, as shown in Fig. 6.1. In unusual cases, three cranes may be required, as shown in Fig. 6.2. These units, each weighing 60 tons, were lifted off the vehicle in a horizontal position (see Fig. 4.1), rotated to a vertical position, then moved into position with two cranes.

A heavy spreader bar, shown in Fig. 6.3, is supporting a 2-story windowwall in the rotated position. The panel is about to be landed and attached to the building. This was a 4-high pickup. The single-point pickup in Fig. 6.4 is an edge pickup and shows a load distributing angle attached by bolts to embedded inserts.

Erecting units of the type shown in Fig. 6.5 requires close tolerances that usually make necessary some sort of guide fixture. The light channel frame just above the workman's knee in Fig. 6.6 is attached to the lower unit already in final position and guides the new unit into its proper place so it can be secured.

Fig. 6.1—The heavy single tee is being lifted into place with two cranes.

EQUIPMENT

Handling and erecting precast concrete is accomplished with a variety of equipment. Crawler cranes are sometimes used, as are tower cranes and occasionally a stiffleg derrick. The rig most used is the truck crane, frequently with a hydraulic boom. These

Fig. 6.2—The 60-ton special precast unit required three cranes to rotate it and set it in place.

Fig. 6.3—Use of a spreader bar minimizes eccentric loading on inserts and simplifies rotation of the precast unit.

Fig. 6.4—Distribution of the load by means of the angle attached to inserts in the end of the unit permits single-line edge pickup. A tag line may be necessary to prevent excessive turning of the unit while in the air.

machines come in capacities ranging from a few tons to 50 tons or more.

The capacity of a crane is the load it can pick up with a certain boom at a certain radius. As the boom is lengthened or the boom angle increased, the safe load decreases. On high-rise buildings cranes work with very long booms; the manufacturer's instructions must be followed as to actual lifting capacity under any given condition. (A capacity chart is given in Fig. 3.10.)

The use and operation of any crane or hoisting equipment is potentially dangerous, and such use is closely regulated by law. Only properly designated persons should be permitted to operate a crane or lifting device, and operators must be licensed according to local regulations. Persons concerned with operation of cranes should be familiar with these laws and regulations as well as safe operating procedures. Excellent sources of information are the "Crane Operators Manual,"[14] and the P & H "Safe Operating Practices."[15] Safety devices are available that give a warning when the crane boom moves within a certain distance of power lines. Another device indicates on a dial in the operator's cab the angle of the boom.

Tower cranes are designed to cover a large area at considerable height, and they are ideal for this purpose. Their capacities are

Fig. 6.5—Numerous steel pipe columns in this building serve to carry the precast concrete mullions shown being installed in Fig. 6.6.

relatively small; they are particularly suitable if there are no heavy members to be hoisted.

When attaching precast concrete to a steel frame building, rarely can the erector count on using the steel erector's crane. Normally there will be too many conflicts. The precast erector should provide his own crane or hoisting equipment, either his own or that of a subcontractor. Cranes, hardware, and rigging are covered in Chapter 3.

Fig. 6.6—Placing cne of the mullions shown in Fig. 6.5 (see also Fig. 5.2). A light steel fixture guides the mullion into place, aligning it with the one previously installed below.

TOLERANCES

The members must be accurately positioned after installation and situated within the specified tolerances, as nearly as possible in the center of their theoretical location on the structure. Care is necessary to assure that cumulative dimensional errors are not permitted to build up. In one case of precast wall frames and joists, it was found that they were over width by about ⅛ in. each; the building length was increased by nearly 3 in. when these units were erected. The importance of proper adherence to tolerances is vividly shown in the building facade in Fig. 6.7.

All temporary handling and lifting devices should be removed as soon as possible. Initial fastening of the unit should be done as rapidly as possible to release the crane for other work. Final tightening of bolts should be done with a torque wrench.

Tolerances will be specified by the Architect/Engineer. The following tolerances are suggested by ACI Committee 533 for erection of wall panels.[16]

Fig. 6.7—The importance of close adherence to tolerances is shown in this building facade consisting of many units of high relief.

1. *Face width of joint*
Panel dimension (normal to joint) 10 ft (3 m) or under .... ±3/16 in. (±5 mm)
Panel dimension (normal to joint) 10 ft (3 m) to 20 ft (6 m) .... +3/16 in. (+5 mm)
                                                             −1/4 in. (−6 mm)
Each additional 10 ft (3 m)
(normal to joint) .... ±1/16 in. (±2 mm)
2. *Joint taper* (panel edges not parallel) .... 1/40 in. (1/2 mm)
                                                             per ft (30 cm)
                                                             length or 1/16 in.
                                                             (2 mm) total, which-
                                                             ever is larger, but
                                                             not greater than
                                                             3/8 in. (9 mm)
3. *Panel alignment*
Jog in alignment of edge .... 1/4 in. (6 mm)
Offset in face of panel (exterior face unless otherwise noted) .... 1/4 in. (6 mm)
4. *Location of openings in wall panels* .... ±1/4 in. (±6 mm)
Some types of window and equipment frames require openings more accurately placed; when this is the case, minimum practical tolerance is .... ±1/8 in. (±3 mm)

TEMPORARY BRACING

Not all precast units require temporary bracing. The drawings show what temporary bracing is necessary to support members until final connections can be made. Some structures require that wind loading be considered when designing temporary bracing.

Wind forces on precast concrete units should be as determined by the design engineer. For computing maximum wind pressures, it can be assumed that a precast unit is a long and narrow flat plate with a maximum drag coefficient $c_d = 1.8$. Wind pressure can then be computed from the following formula:

$$D = 1.8(\tfrac{1}{2}\varrho v^2)A$$

where

$D =$ wind force on a unit, lb
$\varrho =$ mass density of air (at sea level and 59 F, $\varrho = 0.002378$ slugs per cu ft)
$v =$ wind velocity, mph
$A =$ area exposed to the wind, sq ft

This formula can be converted to the following:

$$\varrho = D/A = 0.0046v^2$$

where

$\varrho =$ wind pressure, lb per sq ft
$v =$ wind velocity, mph

Maximum wind velocity to be considered in the design should be determined by the design engineer based on local meteorological data. Wind forces should be considered as acting from any direction, and braces should be designed to take reversal of forces.[17]

Another factor to consider is the stability of the entire structure. At different times during construction, there are periods when the structure is not completely stable, particularly in a building consisting of precast framing units. Periods of this nature can be minimized by providing lateral ties to previously constructed or erected parts of the building (such as shear walls) and completing diaphragms and stiffeners as rapidly as possible along with placing of cast-in-place concrete.

SHIMS

Shims are necessary to level the panels or other precast units while they are being set in place. Members that are to be grouted in place can be set on shims and the void dry-packed later. Members with welded connections can be set on shims while the connection is tack-welded; bolt-connected units can likewise be set on shims.

Shims can be of metal, wood, asbestos fiber, or plastic. Steel shims, if left in place for any length of time, are apt to rust and stain the concrete; for this reason many erectors use the special plastic shims which come in several sizes and thicknesses.

After erection the erector should check to make sure that all bearing surfaces are in full contact with bearing supports. If this is not done, the structure may be weakened by inadequate bearings that go unnoticed.

PANELS

In this category, and classified as panels, are such items as wall panels, curtainwalls, and windowwalls.

Small panels may be transported in a horizontal position on the truck. A four-point pickup can be used by attaching lifting lines to inserts near the top and bottom of the panel, or attaching to lifting bars on top and bottom edges of the panel. The panel is lifted slightly in a horizontal position; then, as soon as it is clear of the truck, the top edge is lifted while the lower edge remains stationary or even drops slightly; the member is rotated until it is vertical, in which position it is hoisted to the required elevation. Normally no special equipment is necessary for rotating the unit, although occasionally a device is developed that serves only one special purpose as shown in Fig. 6.8. The windowwall member, weighing about 7,600 lb, was supported on a tilting frame with lugs at the window head to support the precast concrete without transferring any load to the relatively delicate prestressed dangling mullions. Fig. 6.9 shows a similar panel being hoisted. Note the

Fig. 6.8—A unique solution to the problem of avoiding damage to the relatively small dangling mullions while rotating the member was to place the unit flat on a tilting frame, then tilt to a vertical position and lift into position.

steel spreader attached to the top of the unit. This spreader is attached to coil loop inserts and is used for lifting, being removed as soon as the precast member is landed on the building frame. Panels when erected on a steel frame are usually landed on asbestos polymer pads (similar to those used under bridge girders) and fastened to the steel frame with bolts and clips at the top edge. Figure 6.10 shows panels being attached to a concrete frame. Note the bolts and clips along the top of the panels. The windowwall panel in Fig. 6.11 is 7 ft wide by 67 ft high, covering six stories.

The small panels in Fig. 6.12 are being lifted and set in place with a small hydraulic crane. Note that the panels slip into the vertical grooves between the flanges of the steel H-columns.

Fig. 6.9—A typical edge lift without a spreader bar. Lifting lines are attached to the steel spreader which in turn is fastened to the concrete with inserts in the end of the precast member.

In erecting wall panels, it is important that the joints between panels (both horizontal and vertical) as well as the alignment of the panels be closely controlled so they are uniform in all planes. The architectural excellence of a building exterior depends to a great extent on the uniformity and continuity of joints between the panels and on the panels being aligned in the proper plane.

Fig. 6.10—Bolts in the cast-in-place frame receive clips which hold the precast panels in place.

Frequent checks are necessary while the panels are being erected and fastened in place.

Panels should be protected from welding damage by the use of asbestos sheets or similar nonflammable material while welding is being done. Loose slag should be removed after welding of a joint has been completed, and the weld and other exposed steel should be painted with a rust-inhibitive primer.

Exterior panels are exposed to many conditions that might stain them during construction of the building. Rainwater or water used in construction picks up dirt which will stain the concrete. The general contractor should provide temporary protection as construction proceeds. Dirt, mortar, and debris from concrete placing should not be permitted to remain on the precast concrete and should be washed off with clean water.

Precast wall panels can be designed to incorporate cast-in-place structural units. For example, a column can be formed at the juncture between two adjacent panels, or a spandrel beam can be formed along the top of the panels (Figs. 6.13 and 6.14). In this type of construction the cast-in-place concrete serves as the connection be tween the precast members. For one building in which this con struction was followed, a repetitive procedure was developed which was used on each story of the building as described below.

The building consisted of cast-in-place interior columns, pre cast prestressed beams, and precast slabs on which a 2-in. topping

Fig. 6.11—An unusually long windowwall unit about to be inserted in the six-story opening in the masonry wall.

Fig. 6.12—A small hydraulic crane placing precast panels on a steel frame by inserting them in the grooves in the steel H-columns.

Column form

Fig. 6.13—Precast panels can be manufactured to include a concrete form for a cast-in-place column, as shown in this plan view of the junction between two panels.

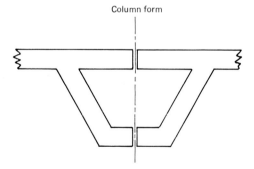

was cast. The topping was placed to within 3 ft of the exterior wall panels. The panels were then set in place and temporarily braced to the existing floor, as in tilt-up construction. A reinforcing steel cage was set in each column form created at the juncture of two panels, and the joint on each side of the form was closed with asbestos-cement strips. Concrete was then placed in the column in the usual manner. Dowels projecting from the bottom of the panels formed the tie-in to the spandrel beam on the panels below, in

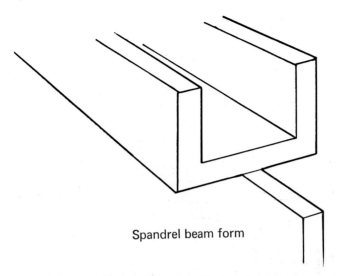

Spandrel beam form

Fig. 6.14—A spandrel beam form can be precast with the wall panel.

which concrete was placed simultaneously with the remainder of the topping concrete.

PRECAST CONCRETE FORMS FOR CAST-IN-PLACE CONCRETE

Precast concrete forms have been used to some extent for hydraulic structures in some countries but have not become popular in the United States, probably because of economic considerations. They have been used for buildings and bridges, one of the commonest uses being for soffit or bottom forms for slabs and decks (Fig. 6.15) in which concrete for the cast-in-place deck is placed directly on the precast slabs. Beam and column forms are being used with increasing frequency. Normal forming techniques can be used, as depicted in Fig. 6.16. Steel columns can be enclosed with flat panels or trough-shaped sections (Fig. 6.16). A highly ornamental column is shown in Fig. 6.17. Storing, handling, and erecting these units requires the same care as any other concrete to avoid damage by staining, breakage, or warping.

After the units have been erected and braced to proper line and grade, form ties can be installed to tie the precast form to the building frame, to other parts of the precast form, or to timber

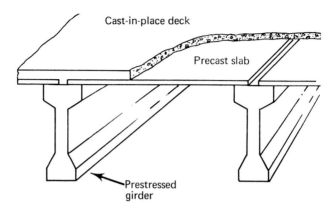

Cast-in-place deck

Precast slab

Prestressed
girder

Fig. 6.15—Thin precast, prestressed slabs can serve as bottom form for cast-in-place deck. Shear transfer devices can be cast in the top of the prestressed girders, extending into cast-in-place deck concrete in the slot between the slab ends. The precast slabs are usually laid on a bed of mortar.

forms. These ties can be attached to embedded anchors or other conventional methods, including attachment to the reinforcement (provided provision was made when the units were cast) or at joints between the panels. Close tolerances in alignment are necessary, especially where edges of units form continuous lines (either vertical or horizontal), to avoid unsightly offsets or noticeable variations in widths of joints. Field welding of connections must be carefully done to avoid burning, staining, or spalling the concrete.

Placing of cast-in-place concrete requires compliance with the best practices in concreting. Special care is necessary to prevent disfiguring the architectural surfaces by spillage of concrete and grout from buckets, chutes, or pipelines; leakage from joints between forms and other elements; or rundown from overfilling the forms. Joints between precast panels can be back-plastered or stopped with a filler to prevent leakage of grout. The filler can be removed later prior to caulking. Placing of concrete should be at a rate normally followed for placing against good plywood forms—generally about 2 ft per hr, depending on temperature and placing conditions. Curing methods should be selected that will not deface the finished surfaces, and the completed work should be protected from further soiling by construction activities. (The report of ACI Committee 347[18] is an excellent source of information on this subject.)

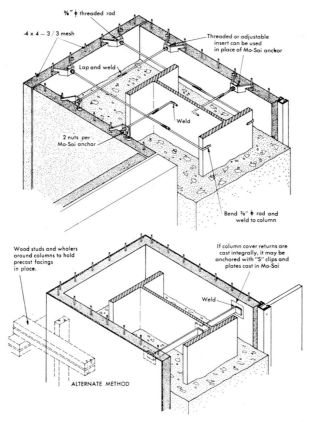

Fig. 6.16—Two methods of using precast concrete members as forms for a cast-in-place concrete column in which a steel column is embedded.

SLAB AND JOIST FLOORS

A common type of precast floor assembly consists of relatively small precast joists spanning between girders or walls, supporting a floor consisting of precast slabs, cast-in-place concrete, or a combination of precast slabs with a cast-in-place concrete topping.

Joists may be of any shape that meets the requirements of the building code and design engineer, the commonest being an I-beam section as shown in Fig. 6.18.

For every job the Architect/Engineer prepares a joist-setting plan, to assure that joists are installed in their proper places and in sequence to facilitate construction. Joists usually rest on a

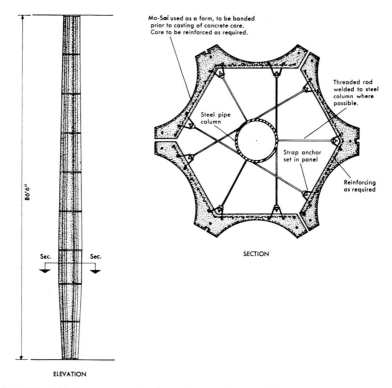

Fig. 6.17—A highly ornamented column form consisting of three precast sections tied with interior ties. The form should be reinforced with straps or bands about the exterior before placing concrete. The bands are subsequently removed after the concrete hardens.

girder or wall (Fig. 6.19). In cases where this construction is not possible, a tension bar hanger may be inserted in the end of the joist when it is cast. Lacking a tension bar, the joist can still be hung by using a metal joist hanger, as shown in Fig. 6.20.

Holes must not be made in joists without the approval of the design engineer. If holes through the web become necessary, they should be no more than 2 in. in diameter and should be drilled as near the middepth of the beam as possible, or at a location of minimum shear.*

A joist and slab floor may consist of cast-in-place slabs placed directly on the joists with the top of the joist embedded $\frac{1}{2}$ in.

* A more general restriction for beams of any size limits the diameter of the hole to not more than $\frac{1}{4}$ the depth of the beam.

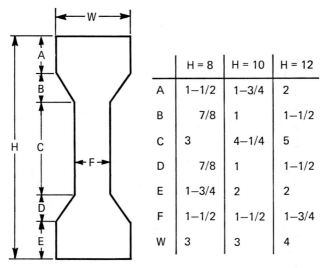

	H = 8	H = 10	H = 12
A	1–1/2	1–3/4	2
B	7/8	1	1–1/2
C	3	4–1/4	5
D	7/8	1	1–1/2
E	1–3/4	2	2
F	1–1/2	1–1/2	1–3/4
W	3	3	4

Fig. 6.18—Small precast joists are usually prestressed and may be 8, 10, or 12 in. in height, proportioned as shown.

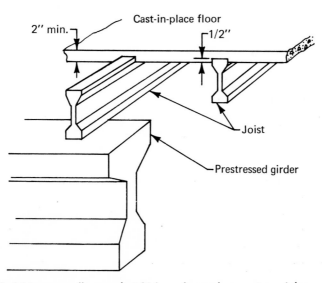

Fig. 6.19—Joists are usually spaced at 36 in. or less and can rest on girders or walls. The top of the joist is embedded ½ in. in the cast-in-place concrete floor.

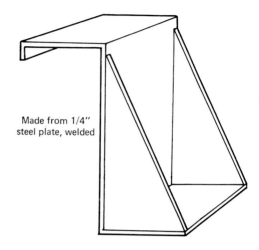

Fig. 6.20—At stairwells and similar locations the end of a joist can be supported by a special hanger hung over a girder or wall. The hanger is dimensioned to fit the joist and other structural units.

Made from 1/4" steel plate, welded

into the slab concrete. Slab thickness is 2 or $2\frac{1}{2}$ in. depending on spacing of joists: 2 in. for spacing of less than 30 in., $2\frac{1}{2}$ in. for spacing of 30 to 36 in. Slabs must be designed to accommodate whatever loads are to be imposed, in accordance with standard design methods; a thickness greater than $2\frac{1}{2}$ in. may be required for certain floors such as one carrying heavy distributed loads. Under concentrated loads such as a partition wall parallel to the joists, the joist spacing can be reduced, or joists can be placed side by side. Therefore, an engineering analysis is necessary when designing any floor.

CORED FLOORS

A cored floor is made up of precast units in which part of the cross section of the unit has been left out to achieve a lightweight unit at little or no sacrifice in strength (Fig. 6.21). Some units are wet-cast in required lengths, others are cast or extruded on long beds and sawed into whatever lengths are necessary for any particular installation.

Another type of cored floor is made up of masonry units strung on steel rods which are tensioned sufficiently to prestress the blocks and provide flexural strength to the member (Fig. 6.22). The rods bear against steel bearing plates on the ends of the string of blocks.

Construction loads, including the weight of fresh cast-in-place floor topping, should be considered when determining the need

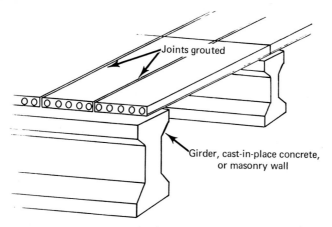

Joints grouted

Girder, cast-in-place concrete, or masonry wall

Fig. 6.21—Cored floor units, which may span 30 ft or more, may rest on concrete or steel girders, block walls, or concrete walls.

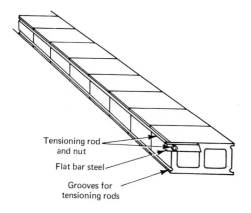

Fig. 6.22—A type of post-tensioned unit can be made by stressing four steel rods to introduce sufficient compression in the masonry blocks to give the unit flexural strength.

Tensioning rod and nut

Flat bar steel

Grooves for tensioning rods

for shoring beneath precast floor slabs. Some users specify a maximum span of 8 ft, but this should be determined for the type and size of floor slabs being erected and the superimposed loads.

Prior to erection of floor units, the bearing surface on top of wall or girder must be true to line and grade and should be checked by the installer.

In some buildings, bond beams are cast-in-place on masonry walls at each floor level, with weld plates positioned in the beams. Inserts in the bottom of the cored units are welded to the plate in the bond beam. Another method is to set an anchor bar vertically in the concrete of the wall or bond beam, bent to enter into one of the cores of the slab where it is concreted in place or bent into the grout space between slabs (Fig. 6.23).

Occasional practice on masonry walls is to use a ⅛-in. thick strip of hardboard for bearing. Slabs that can be set on concrete or structural steel are landed directly on the bearing and pulled up tight to keep them at right angles to the bearing wall or girder. If a girder is a support for two bays, the load must be kept fairly uniform on both sides of the girder by placing slabs alternately on opposite sides to prevent twisting or rotation. Hangers for pipe, conduit, and suspended ceiling can be inserted in the space between the slabs before the slabs are finally aligned along the end and pulled together, or they can be inserted in holes cast or drilled in the slab.

The next operation is leveling the deck. This is done from the bottom side, inserting wedges where necessary to raise a slab so the bottom surfaces are even. Another method used by one manufacturer is to embed wire eyes at the edge of the slabs. While one workman raises the low slab, another man on top drives a wedge from the high slab through the eye on the low slab to hold the two slabs in vertical alignment. The eyes are subsequently bent down after the deck has been grouted.

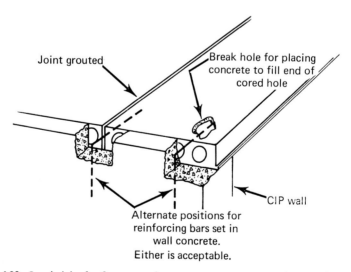

Fig. 6.23—Cored slabs for floor or roof rest on a grout or mortar layer and are tied into the wall with reinforcing bars placed vertically in the wall concrete, then bent into the joint between floor units or extended into the void in the unit. The steel is grouted or concreted in place.

Grouting is accomplished by first filling the ends of the joints between slabs with stiff mortar to keep the grout from running out the ends. Next a 1:3 grout with sufficient water to spread easily is spread with brooms and squeegees over the surface of the deck; all spaces between the cored slabs must be filled. If the opening between slabs is excessively wide, it may be necessary to tape the joint to prevent excessive loss of grout. Ordinarily this is not necessary. Drippings of grout on the underside of the deck can be removed by brushing or washing down with a light spray of water before the grout sets. Walls and floors should be cleaned. After the grout has set for a day, the wedges can be removed and eyes (if any were used) bent down. Bearings should be inspected to make sure the slab has full bearing. If necessary, dry-pack mortar can be tamped in any open spaces. The deck can now be used by other trades.

Holes can be cast or drilled in the bottom or ceiling side of the slab provided they are at least $1\frac{3}{4}$ in. from the longitudinal steel and below the void or hollow part of the unit. No channeling or grooving can be done in the top of a unit except over a support. Reinforcement should not be cut. Any cutting or drilling must be approved beforehand by the design engineer.

The bottom side of most slab floors can serve as the ceiling of the story below. Joints between slabs should be caulked and the caulking finished to a smooth, concave groove. Filling of voids and patching should be finished, then paint applied as specified by the paint manufacturer. An acoustical ceiling can be sprayed on if proper precautions are taken to insure bond. Hangers inserted in the joints between slabs during erection can serve to carry a suspended ceiling.

CAULKING

Joints occur in buildings between precast concrete and cast-in-place concrete, between precast units, and between concrete and miscellaneous installed hardware such as metal window and door frames. Occasionally joints are designed and constructed to be weathertight, such as those shown in Fig. 5.16. Most joints, however, are not intended to be weathertight until they have been caulked.

Nonelastic grouts are not usually specified for exposed joints, because movement resulting from temperature changes will cause the grout to crack and spall. However, portland cement grout is frequently used at the base of tilt-up panels and other panels that are set on shims.

Other than the grouts (which are rarely used), joint materials consist of oil-base caulking compounds or mastics and elastomeric materials such as polysulfides, certain epoxies, urethane, acrylics, and butyl sealants.

Caulking compounds vary in quality and performance depending on formulation, brand, and application techniques. Workmanship in application is an important factor affecting the performance of a compound. Properly applied caulking should remain watertight for many years, although the best will eventually dry out and have to be renewed.

A backup filler is necessary in the joint to control the depth of sealant and to prevent bond between the sealant and the back of the joint. The backup should compress and expand with movement of the panels or other elements at the joint and must be compatible with the sealant. It should not stain the sealant, as this may bleed through and cause discoloration of the joint. A rod or strand of sponge material is commonly specified—usually a foamed polymer of some kind such as styrene, ethylene, urethane, or polyvinyl chloride, or sometimes a synthetic rubber. Fibrous glass is sometimes used, or supporting material such as fiberboard, cork, mortar, or wood. Bond between the sealant and backup can be prevented by laying strips of polyethylene film or masking tape over the bottom of the joint before application of the sealant.

Joint surfaces must be clean and dry, accomplished by the use of solvents, wire brushes, or air brushing. If the bond breaker used in casting the concrete is such that the residue on the concrete surfaces inhibits good adhesion, it may be necessary to sandblast and wash the contact surfaces. No sealant should ever be applied directly over a silicone waterproofer.

Whatever sealant is used, the manufacturer's instructions should be followed. In some cases a primer is recommended. The primer should be allowed to cure before application of the sealant. Most specifications require the use of an air or power-activated gun for application of the sealant, using a nozzle of the proper size for the joint being filled. The joint should be completely filled, then tooled slightly concave. No solution of any kind should be used on the tools, although slight wetting with clean water is acceptable. Tooling improves the appearance of the joint, eliminates air pockets, and provides maximum contact at joint interfaces.

Proper scheduling of joint sealing is important. The subcontractor can work more efficiently if all other work that might damage or contaminate joint surfaces has been completed. If possible, sealant application should be scheduled for seasonal periods when joints are at their normal size; otherwise joints may be underfilled or overfilled. Manufacturers of sealants recommend application of their materials at above 40 F (4 C); surface moisture is more likely to be present at lower temperatures, and most sealants will not adhere to a wet surface. If it becomes necessary to apply the sealant during cold weather, the surface must be clean as for normal application and must be free of frost or condensation. Wipe the area to be sealed with a quick-drying solvent just before sealing. Heat the area if possible, or at least be sure the sealant is slightly warm when applied.

Cleanup of spills and smears should be done as the work progresses, since it is much easier to remove fresh sealant than sealant that has aged and cured. A comprehensive discussion of joint sealants is included in Reference 19.

GLAZING

In a few cases wall panels containing window openings have been glazed before erection, but by far the vast majority of glazing is done after the precast concrete has been erected. This glass, unfortunately, is subject to damage from subsequent construction activity, especially that which continues on upper floors of the building.

There have been reports of glass being damaged by alkalies leached out of the concrete. Alkali and fluorides washed off floors that have had a hardening treatment will etch glass if left on for any appreciable period. This etching has the appearance of white streaks on the glass. Other contamination results from deleterious material picked up by the atmosphere, rain, or snow and deposited on the glass. Dirty water from cleanup activities, mortar dust from plastering and fireproofing, and roofing tar fumes are among the sources of damaging substances.

Some contractors state that the tinted glass now used in so many buildings is subject to etching by any material that remains on the glass for a prolonged period—not only accumulations of dirt and dust but markings on the glass, labels, and even rings left by suction cups. Adhesives and gasket lubricants may cause trouble. Debris from welding is another source of contamination.

Glazing should be delayed as long as possible to minimize the exposure. Once the glass is installed, it should be kept clean by frequent washing. It is especially important to wash the glass after a rain or after cleaning operations on the stories above.

If washing with water and soap and rinsing with clean water does not clean the glass, the glass manufacturer should be consulted. Whatever method is used, its effect on the window surrounds and on the concrete should be considered. For example, washing with 4% hydrofluoric acid has been suggested but requires great care to prevent damage to other parts of the building.

CLEANING

After completion of all work that may have an effect on the panels, the panels will probably have to be cleaned, especially if made of white cement. Sometimes all that is necessary is to wash them with *clean* water. If more vigorous cleaning is indicated, a soap-and-water cleaning with stiff fiber brushes is effective. If this is not sufficient, it may be necessary to use a weak (5%) muriatic acid wash, after first thoroughly wetting the surface with clean water. Precautions must be taken to protect other surfaces when using acid. Thorough washing and rinsing are necessary. The acid treatment may etch the surface, especially if the acid remains on the surface for more than a few seconds, so it is a good idea to try it on an inconspicuous spot first.

Several commercial cleaning compounds on the market are effective against certain stains. With any of these, make a small trial first to see what the effect will be.

Metal that surrounds the windows is sometimes etched and discolored by contaminating substances. When this happens, care must be taken so any cleanup does not look worse than the original damage. Especially on aluminum or painted metal, the use of harsh scouring powders should be avoided. Aluminum surrounds are subject to attack by acids and alkalis. Although most aluminum trim has been anodized by the mill or fabricator to prevent corrosion, cement mortar, if left on for any length of time, is likely to corrode the metal, and acid cleaning agents may also cause trouble. If the aluminum has been stained, it should be rubbed gently with a polish such as automobile polish. Steel wool, kitchen cleansers, and scouring pads should be used only with great care, since they might scratch and etch the aluminum.

APPENDIX A
CONCRETE AND MORTAR MIXTURES

Throughout this book mention is made of the use of grout, mortar, and concrete. This is usually in connection with repair of damaged units, the use of bedding material for supporting the units in the structure, and for filling voids or joints.

Job site repair of damaged members presents a serious problem in esthetics; matching the original color and texture can be difficult. Therefore, when repair becomes necessary under these circumstances, it is suggested that the precaster be consulted for assistance. He can furnish the proper materials and proportions for making the patch mixtures to match the precast units.

When it is necessary to proportion concrete, as for cast-in-place columns for tilt-up, the specifications should govern the ready-mixed concrete producer and laboratory in their choice of materials and proportions. ACI has published recommended practices that cover all phases of concrete construction, including proportioning, mixing, placing, and curing concrete. The recommendations of these publications should be observed. Because of the great variety of job site conditions, it is not possible to make specific recommendations for concreting.

The terms grout and mortar are sometimes used interchangeably, although in practice there is a slight difference.

Mortar—One part cement, $2\frac{1}{2}$ parts mason's or plastering sand (by weight or volume), and sufficient water to make a plastic, workable mortar. Avoid wet, soupy mortar. The consistency used by brick masons is about right.

Grout or grouting—Mortar, or the placing of mortar in a cavity or bedding. In common usage, grout is generally of a wetter consistency than mortar so it can fill cavities between units.

Dry-pack—One part cement, $2\frac{1}{2}$ parts mason's or plastering sand, and sufficient water to make the material moist enough to form a ball when squeezed in the hand. The mortar should not exude water when squeezed. Dry-pack is placed into position by tamping or packing with rammers, sticks, or similar blunt instruments.

If mason's sand is not available, a suitable substitute can be made by screening concrete sand through a No. 12 or 16 screen.

APPENDIX B
CONVERSION FACTORS—U.S. AND CANADIAN
CUSTOMARY TO SI (METRIC)*

To convert from	to	multiply by
Length		
foot	meter (m)	0.3048E†
inch	centimeter (cm)	2.54E
yard	meter (m)	0.9144E
mile (statute)	kilometer (km)	1.609
Area		
square foot	square meter (m²)	0.0929
square inch	square centimeter (cm²)	6.451
square yard	square meter (m²)	0.8361
Volume (capacity)		
cubic foot	cubic meter (m³)	0.02832
gallon (U.S. liquid)‡	cubic meter (m³)§	0.003785
gallon (Can. liquid)‡	cubic meter (m³)§	0.004546
ounce (U.S. liquid)	cubic centimeter (cm³)	29.57
Force		
kilogram-force	newton (N)	9.807
kip	kilogram-force (kgf)	453.6
kip	newton (N)	4,448
pound-force	kilogram-force (kgf)	0.4536
pound-force	newton (N)	4.448
Pressure or Stress (Force per Area)		
kilogram-force/square meter	newton/square meter (N/m²)	9.807
kip/square inch (ksi)	kilogram-force/square centimeter (kgf/cm²)	70.31
pound-force/square foot	kilogram-force/square meter (kgf/m²)	4.882

131

To convert from   to   multiply by

pound-force/square foot ....newton/square meter (N/m^2).............. 47.88
pound-force/square inch (psi) .....kilogram-force/square centimeter (kgf/cm^2).. 0.07031
pound-force/square inch (psi) ....newton/square meter (N/m^2)..............6,895

Bending Moment or Torque

inch-pound-force ....meter-kilogram-force (m-kgf)............... 0.01152
inch-pound-force ....newton-meter (Nm)...................... 0.1130
foot-pound-force ....meter-kilogram-force (m-kgf)............. 0.1383
foot-pound-force ....newton-meter (Nm)...................... 1.356
meter-kilogram-force ....newton-meter (Nm)...................... 9.807

Mass

ounce-mass (avdp) ....gram (g).................................. 28.35
pound-mass (avdp) ....kilogram (kg)............................. 0.4536
ton (metric) ....kilogram (kg)............................1,000E
ton (short, 2,000 lbm) ....kilogram (kg)............................. 907.2

Mass per Volume

pound-mass/cubic foot ....kilogram/cubic meter (kg/m^3).............. 16.02
pound-mass/cubic yard ....kilogram/cubic meter (kg/m^3).............. 0.5933
pound-mass/gallon (U.S.)‡.......kilogram/cubic meter (kg/m^3)§............. 119.8
pound-mass/gallon (Can.)‡.......kilogram/cubic meter (kg/m^3)§............ 99.78

Temperature∥

deg Celsius (C) ....kelvin (K)...........................$t_K = (t_C + 273.15)$
deg Fahrenheit (F) ....kelvin (K).......................$t_K = (t_F + 459.67)/1.8$
deg Fahrenheit (F) ....deg Celsius (C)......................$t_C = (t_F - 32)/1.8$

---

* This selected list gives practical conversion factors of units found in concrete technology. The reference source for information on SI units and more exact conversion factors is "Metric Practice Guide" ASTM E 380.

The International System of Measurement (SI) is the currently recommended form of the metric system. However, since measurement of concrete products in centimeters and of stress and pressure in kilograms-force per unit area is common in many "metric" countries, these units may be used in ACI publications even though they do not conform strictly to the International System. ACI policy on units of measurement can be found in the Institute's Publication Policy or Technical Committee Manual.

Symbols of metric units are given in parentheses.
† E indicates that the factor given is exact.
‡ One U.S. gallon equals 0.8327 Canadian gallon.
§ One liter (cubic decimeter) equals 0.001 m³ or 1,000 cm³.
∥ These factors convert one temperature reading to another and include the necessary scale corrections. To convert a difference in temperature from Fahrenheit degrees to Celsius or kelvin degrees, divide by 1.8 only, i.e., a change from 70 to 88 F represents a change of 18 F deg or 18/1.8 = 10 C deg. To convert deg C to deg F, $t_F = 1.8t_C + 32$.

References

1. Peterson, J. L., "History and Development of Precast Concrete in the United States," ACI JOURNAL, *Proceedings* V. 50, No. 6, Feb. 1954, pp. 477–496.

2. Yamasaki, Minoru, "ACI Headquarters Presented a Challenge in Concrete," ACI JOURNAL, *Proceedings* V. 55, No. 4, Oct. 1958, pp. 419–426.

3. "U.S. Looks to Europe in Systems Building Drive," *Engineering News-Record*, V. 183, Oct. 30, 1969, p. 62.

4. "System Building: Gigantic Challenge and Opportunity," *Concrete Products*, V. 69, No. 10, Oct. 1966, p. 60.

5. "Building Systems Get Firm Grip on Construction," *Engineering News-Record*, V. 185, Oct. 22, 1970, p. 96.

6. ACI Committee 506, "Recommended Practice for Shotcreting (ACI 506-66)," American Concrete Institute, Detroit, 1966, 26 pp. Also, *ACI Manual of Concrete Practice*, Part 3, 1968.

7. ACI-ASCE Committee 512, "Suggested Design of Joints and Connections in Precast Structural Concrete," ACI JOURNAL, *Proceedings* V. 61, No. 8, Aug. 1964, pp. 921–938.

8. ACI Committee 318, "Building Code Requirements for Reinforced Concrete (ACI 318-71)," American Concrete Institute, Detroit, 1971, 78 pp.

9. "Recommended Practices for Welding Reinforcing Steel, Metal Inserts, and Connections in Reinforced Concrete Construction," AWS D12.1-61, American Welding Society, New York, 1961.

10. *Uniform Building Code*, International Conference of Building Officials, Whittier, Calif., 1973, Section 2314(k)5.

11. Birkeland, Philip W., and Birkeland, Halvard W., "Connections in Precast Concrete Construction," ACI JOURNAL, *Proceedings* V. 63, No. 3, Mar. 1966, pp. 345–368.

12. "PCMAC Connections Manual," Prestressed Concrete Manufacturers Association of California, Inc., LaMesa, Calif.

13. "Mo-Sai Design Details," The Mo-Sai Institute, Inc., Redmond, Wash.

14. "Crane Operator's Manual," Crane Manufacturers Association of America, Inc., Washington, D.C.

15. "Safe Operating Practices for Crane and Hoist Users," Harischfeger, Milwaukee, Wis.

16. ACI Committee 533, "Fabrication, Handling, and Erection of Precast Concrete Wall Panels," ACI JOURNAL, *Proceedings* V. 67, No. 4, Apr. 1970, pp. 310–340.

17. Peterson, J. L., "Design and Construction Guide for Precast Structural Concrete," ACI JOURNAL, *Proceedings* V. 59, No. 9, Sept. 1962, pp. 1179–1204.

18. ACI Committee 347, "Recommended Practice for Concrete Formwork (ACI 347-68)," American Concrete Institute, Detroit, 1968, 50 pp. Also, *ACI Manual of Concrete Practice*, Part 1, 1968.

19. ACI Committee 504, "Guide to Joint Sealants for Concrete Structures," ACI JOURNAL, *Proceedings* V. 67, No. 7, July 1970, pp. 489–536.

Index